Contents

My People

Abba Eban's
History of the Jews
VOLUME I

ADAPTED BY DAVID BAMBERGER

by
Miriam P. Kurinsky

BEHRMAN HOUSE, INC., PUBLISHERS
NEW YORK, NEW YORK

ISBN: 0-87441-329-X

1 2 3 4 5 85 84 83 82 81 80

Book designed and illustrated by Marvin Friedman

*To Dov and Jason and all the rest of
the Diaspora in Missoula, Montana*

My People

Abba Eban's
History of the Jews
VOLUME I

Chapter 1

THE ANCIENT WORLD

HOW JUDAISM TOOK ROOT WITH AN IDEA

Fill in the blanks with words from those listed below.

The first great period of Jewish history lasted almost _2000_
years, from _2000 B.C.E_ to _165 BCE_. It is called the
Biblical Period. It began with a man the Bible calls Abraham
who became possessed with the idea of _One God_
One God. Abraham was said to come from the area known as
Mesopotamia, which is 1000 miles east of Egypt. According to the
Bible, Abraham at first lived in the city of _Ur_. The Bible
says that he later moved to the city of _Haran_. He left this city
at the age of 75 when God told him to journey southwest to Canaan,
where He promised him a homeland for his people. Abraham
traveled with his wife _Sarah_ and his nephew _Lot_.
They settled in Canaan to live among the _Canaanites_. Today this
land is inhabited by _Israelis_. Abraham's family moved to
Egypt, possibly because of a famine in the new homeland,
but later they returned to the "Promised Land." (After the Exodus,
which you will read about in Chapter 2, the Hebrew tribes
descended from the family of Abraham returned to settle the land
and became a _nation_.)

165 B.C.E.	Damascus	Syrians	Sarah
Mesopotamia	Lot	Ur	Canaanites
1000 B.C.E.	Canaan	2000 B.C.E.	One God
Israelis	Biblical	Haran	prehistoric
nation	2000	Egypt	Ruth

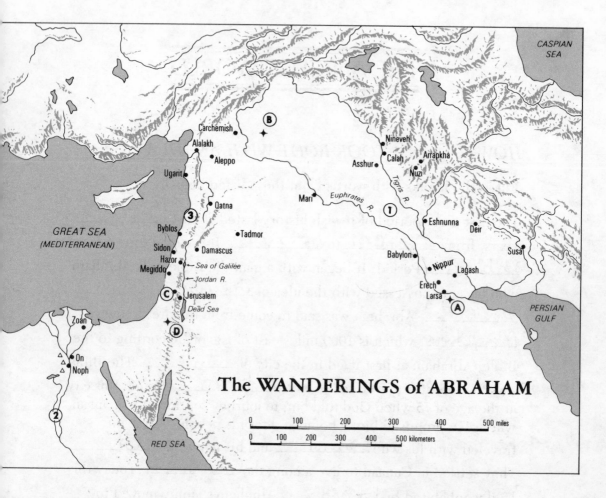

The **WANDERINGS of ABRAHAM**

1. Name the major land areas which figure in the story of Abraham's journey. (They are shown on the map as 1, 2, and 3.)

1. _Meopotamia_
2. _Egypt_
3. _Canaan_

2. Abraham first lived in Babylonia in (a) _Ur_. His family later settled in (b) _Haran_. His journey to the Promised Land led him to (c) _Shechem_. Finally he settled in (d) _Beersheba_

Draw a line connecting these places to show his route. (Did you remember to include his trip to Egypt?)

THE EMPIRES AND THE NATIONS

True or false?   (T) (F)

1. Egypt and Mesopotamia had highly developed civilizations, including organized central governments, long before the Jewish people came into existence.   (T) F

2. In these civilizations, hundreds of different kinds of idols were worshipped in religious ceremonies with burnt offerings and sometimes human sacrifices.   (T) F

3. The three ruling ancient empires of Egypt, Assyria, and Babylonia were all models of good government.   T (F)

4. The Persians conquered the old empires and allowed religious freedom for two centuries until cruel tyrants took over.   (T) F

5. The Greeks, who conquered the Persians, were never tolerant of the Jews.   T (F)

6. The Maccabees revolted and expelled the Greek army from Israel.   (T) F

Place in order. In the boxes, number the following empires in the order in which each came to dominate the ancient Near East, from 1 to 6.

Assyrian   2
Greek   5
Babylonian   3
Roman   6
Egyptian   1
Persian   4

3

THE CALENDAR

1. What do these letters stand for?

   B.C. _Before Christ_

   A.D. _Anno Domini_

   B.C.E. _Before Common Era_

   C.E. _Common Era_

2. Explain why many Jews prefer to use B.C.E. and C.E. rather than B.C. and A.D. to name dates in history.

   Because we don't believe in Christ

3. The Jewish calendar begins with: (check one)

   a. The first day of creation in the Bible.
   b. The birth of Abraham.
   c. The Exodus.

Chapter 2

"LIKE THE OTHER NATIONS"

A PEOPLE IN BONDAGE

Unscramble the scrambled words.

Still not a nation, but linked by their belief in One God and the
(D)R P O M S I(E) Land, Hebrews left the harsh land of N N C A A A
and migrated to G Y P T E to make a living. At first they prospered
and were free to follow their beliefs, but under cruel
H A P R O A H(S) they were (X)T A D E, then enslaved. Like pack
animals they carried heavy stones to build M(U)N E O(O)M N T S
ordered by A M R S A S E to symbolize his power as a god.

Combine the circled letters. They should form the six-letter word
representing the event which we remember at the Passover Seder,
E X O D U S.

Use this as your work area

A FREE PEOPLE FINDS A LAW TO LIVE BY

Fill in the blanks with words from those listed below.

The Israelites took their first step toward nationhood when their great leader, _Moses_, led them out of bondage. Their flight, known as the _Exodus_, took place around the year _1225 BCE_. The Biblical story of how the _Red Sea_ parted to allow the _refugees_ to escape their Egyptian pursuers is taken as a legend by most people. But archaeological evidence shows that large numbers of Semites did escape from _Egypt_ to _Canaan_ in the ~~1000~~ _13th_ century B.C.E. The Israelites believed they were rescued by God and that His ~~Bible~~ _covenant_ with them promised them His protection only as long as they followed His Law. The Bible tells us that God presented the _Ten Commandments_ to them through Moses at _Sinai_. God's Law gave the Israelites new _ethical_ responsibilities. They finally took control of their promised homeland by about _1000_ B.C.E., more than 200 years after the Exodus.

1225 B.C.E.	Abraham	Exodus	Sinai
thirteenth	ethical	refugees	Canaan
1000	Isaac	Ten Commandments	Red Sea
100 B.C.E.	Moses	covenant	Egypt
eleventh	Joseph	Bible	Babylon

A NATION BEGINS TO TAKE FORM

In Chapter 1 we learned that the Hebrews were held together by the belief in One God and the Promised Land. Now, linked by sacred law and filled with a new self-confidence, the Hebrews returned to Canaan. Show what you know about the settling of Canaan by answering the following **multiple choice questions** (check one).

1. Into how many tribes were the Hebrews divided?

   a. seven
   b. thirteen
   c. twelve

2. The Hebrews

   a. always had one leader.
   b. settled under various leaders in different parts of Canaan.

3. The Hebrews

   a. all had the same religious practices.
   b. differed in the ways they worshipped.

4. The tribes

   a. rejected the superstitions of the Canaanites and Philistines.
   b. often participated in superstitious practices.

5. Hebrew tribal chiefs are called "shoftim" in the Bible. This word means

   a. caretakers
   b. judges
   c. tax collectors

6. The most important of the shoftim was

   a. Samuel
   b. Samson
   c. Joseph

7. Some of the shoftim were also prophets. A prophet in the Biblical sense

   a. predicts the future.
   b. carries messages from God.

PRETEND YOU WERE THERE

Suppose you were a typical girl or boy your own age who lived in the Biblical Period. Describe your daily life, your education or lack of education, your food, clothing, language, or anything else you can remember from the textbook.

A NATION RULED BY KINGS

We learn in this chapter that Saul became the first king of Israel, followed by David and Solomon, and that the Hebrews got what they wanted, a nation "like the other nations."

Name the king.

1. A moody man who ruled for 20 years. Led battles against enemy nations, but had no standing army. Collected no taxes. King

2. Started as a shepherd. Warrior with flair for music and poetry. Reigned for 40 years. Enlarged Hebrew territory through conquest. Established Jerusalem. Very powerful, but did not become a dictator. King _____

3. Built Temple. Known for his wisdom. Yet caused discontent by overtaxing the people and using forced labor to satisfy his desire for buildings and monuments. Encouraged trade with other nations. King _____

A KINGDOM DIVIDED

Differences in beliefs and allegiances have divided nations and caused civil wars throughout human history. Briefly explain the geographical, political, and religious reasons for the split between the kingdoms of Judah and Israel. _____

_____

_____

GOD MAKES HIS WISHES KNOWN

Complete the sentences.

1. Under the leadership of Moses, the Hebrews learned that God's Law is more powerful than that of any king. This belief has helped the Jewish people survive because _____

_____

_____.

2. Pagan superstitions threatened Judaism because _____

_____

_____.

3. The Hebrews put such great trust in the leadership and judge-

ment of the shoftim because _____
_____
_____.

4. The idea that the Israelites were a "chosen people" kept their spirit of nationhood alive even after the ancient Hebrews lost their nation because _____
_____
_____.

Chapter 3

REVOLUTIONARIES IN THE STREETS

IN THE NORTHERN KINGDOM

Hand-written scrolls were used to record events in Biblical times, and few people knew how to read. But imagine that about the year 750 B.C.E. newspapers did exist, and that one called the Beth-El Gazette ran the following editorial denouncing the first of the great Hebrew prophets.

A PROPHET SETS THE STAGE

A wild-eyed Hebrew has appeared in Beth-El with revolutionary ideas. He is condemning nations that oppress other nations. He is trying to make people believe that the "One God" of the Israelites has told him that the poor are entitled to the same treatment as the rich, and he claims that rich people must share their wealth with the poor. Even worse, he criticizes priests. He says their rituals are meaningless because the priests are blind to injustice. He predicts that the Hebrews will be wiped out because they have broken faith with their God. We warn this troublemaker—you are asking for it! Go back to Judah!

Fill in the blanks from the words below.

1. Beth-El was a city in the __Northern kingdom__.

2. The prophet was named __Amos__.

3. Few believed him when he warned that God would use the __Asyrian__ army as a tool to punish the Israelites.

4. Israelites practiced idolatry because they hoped pagan gods would help them prosper in their major occupation, __farming__.

11

5. This prophet taught that God wants righteousness more than _rituals_

6. The teachings and predictions of the prophets are recorded in the _Bible_.

7. In 721 B.C.E. this prophet's prediction came true: the northern tribes were attacked. Those Israelites who survived were driven east to the area of _Mesopotamia_ in the fertile crescent.

8. It is believed that these exiled survivors were the _ten_ lost tribes of Israel.

Ezekiel	fishing	tablets	Assyrian
rituals	Amos	holidays	Isaiah
trading	Persian	Mesopotamia	farming
Bible	ten	Northern Kingdom	thirteen

IN JUDAH

Some years later, the following news story might have broken in Judah. (Since there were no newspapers then, we use the Bible as our source.)

PROPHET OF LAMENTATION ARRESTED!

The prophet Jeremiah was arrested today after making a fiery speech in the Jerusalem marketplace. The crowd mocked him after he called the people of Judah hypocrites. He lamented their wickedness and idolatry, declaring that God was angry with them and would no longer protect Hebrews from war, famine, and pestilence. He predicted that God would punish them by destroying their Temple and the state. Jeremiah was taken to prison, where he is now being held on a charge of treason.

True or false?   (T) (F)

1. Jeremiah was happy to be a prophet.   T **F**

12

2. He foretold that God would eventually grant the Hebrews a homeland.   (T) F

3. He wished he could stop himself from speaking the words which made people laugh at him.   (T) F

4. He predicted that the Jews would be exiled to Babylonia. (T) F

5. Assyria was still a great power when Jeremiah preached. T (F)

6. The Temple was destroyed by the Babylonians.   (T) F

THE PROPHETS SHAPE JEWISH VALUES

Underline the words in parentheses which make each sentence correct.

1. Jeremiah taught the ideal of personal (responsibility) (privacy) (property).

2. Jeremiah said that each person is capable of becoming a (rich) (just) (powerful) person.

3. He predicted that the armies of (Nebuchadnezzar) (Antiochus) (Herod) would drive the Hebrews from Judah.

4. Years after Jeremiah made his predictions, the Hebrews understood that God had punished them by (exile) (Diaspora) (imprisonment) because they had disobeyed Him and broken the (covenant) (Sabbath) (fast).

5. The prophets Isaiah and Micah scolded the people for (not obeying authority) (mistreating the poor) (enjoying life too much).

6. The words carved into a wall at the United Nations which predict world peace were written by the prophet (Jeremiah) (Micah) (Isaiah).

Columns I and II list some values taught by the Hebrew prophets. **In the blank space next to each item in Column II, write the number of the item in Column I that is closest in meaning.**

I	II
1. helping the poor	duty __9__
2. monotheism	non-discrimination __3__
3. no special privileges for social rank	fair play __4__
4. equal treatment for the poor	freedom __7__
5. righteousness	One God __2__
6. justice	equality under law __6__
7. liberty	charity __1__
8. world peace	ethics and morality __5__
9. personal responsibility	non-militancy __8__

THE PROPHETS BRING HOPE FROM GOD

1. The Bible says that after the exile, the prophet Ezekiel, as God's spokesman, foretold that the Lord God *will open your graves*. What did he mean by this? _____

_____

_____

2. What did Second Isaiah mean when he wrote, *Bid Jerusalem take heart.* _____

_____

_____

3. Why, according to Second Isaiah, did God punish the Jews and then save them? _____

_____

_____

4. On what occasion in modern history, of momentous importance to the state of Israel, did three world leaders quote Isaiah?

_____

_____

5. Isaiah said, *And they shall beat their swords into plowshares, and their spears into pruninghooks.* What would happen then?

_____

_____

SOMETHING TO THINK ABOUT

Suppose you knew a boy or girl who attended synagogue faithfully yet was a bully to his or her peers. Would you say that such a person was a good Jew? Why?

Chapter 4

A NATION REBORN

RETURN OF THE EXILES

All but two of the following statements are correct. **Circle the numbers next to the *wrong* ones.**

1. The Hebrews exiled to Babylonia had a comfortable life under Persian rule.

2. Jews enjoyed religious freedom in Babylonia.

3. In 539 B.C.E., all the Hebrews quickly returned to Zion.

4. After an 800-mile trip back to Jerusalem, the pilgrims found the city in ruins.

5. Filled with enthusiasm for rebuilding their homeland, the Hebrews started work on a new Temple.

6. Work halted, but inspired by the prophets Haggai and Zechariah, the people completed the Temple 23 years later.

7. The new Temple was as impressive as the one built by King Solomon which had been destroyed by the Babylonians.

8. The Israelites suffered from a lack of communal leadership until Nehemiah arrived.

9. Intermarriage with non-Hebrews weakened the unity of the Israelites.

NEHEMIAH AND EZRA REVIVE ISRAEL

Nehemiah left court life in the Persian capital in 445 B.C.E. to heed a strong inner call to restore Judah physically and reform her spiritually. Ezra had come from Babylonia a few years earlier, hoping to rekindle in the Hebrews a love for God's Law. **Next to each word or group of words on the following list, briefly describe the changes that occurred in Judah under Nehemiah's rule and Ezra's influence.**

a. religious education _____

b. holiday observance _____

c. enslavement of poor people _____

d. national defense _____

e. ethical life _____

f. intermarriage _____

g. conversion _____

h. pagan practices _____

A UNIFYING SPIRIT

1. How did the synagogue create a democratic spirit among Jews?

2. How did the Jews' use of the synagogue influence other religions?

3. Under Persian rule, the children of Abraham came to be known as Jews—from the word "Judah." What forces helped to unify them during this period?

THE JEW IN ANCIENT GREECE

History shows that most Jews clung to their religious beliefs and traditions in ancient Greece despite the attractions of Hellenic culture. **After each sentence fragment in Column II, place the number of the matching item in Column I that makes a complete and correct sentence about Jewish life under Greek rule.**

I	II
1. Few Jews became sculptors because of	the comforts of Greek life. ___3___
2. The Jewish belief that every person is basically good contradicted	the gloomier side of Greek philosophy. ___1___
3. The Jewish belief that truth is available to everyone through the Torah conflicted with	Greek customs conflicted with Jewish traditions. ___4___
4. Many Jews rejected Greek ways because	the restriction against making graven images. ___2___
5. Some Jews compromised their religious beliefs in exchange for	the Greek idea that truth was available only to a few scholars. ___3___

JEWISH REBELLION

On the 25th of Kislev, 165 B.C.E., the Jews won a great victory for religious freedom when the Maccabees captured Jerusalem. **Fill in the blanks.**

1. The rebel army was led by ___Judah___.

2. He was the son of ___Mattias___, who started the rebellion.

3. After many victories, using guerrilla tactics, the rebels triumphed

18

over the more powerful forces of the Greek tyrant _Antiches_

4. The victorious Maccabees cleansed the _temple_ in Jerusalem.

5. This event is celebrated by the holiday of _Hannakah_

SOMETHING TO THINK ABOUT

Why was the translation of the Bible into Greek so important to Jews and to the rest of the world?

Chapter 5

THE ROMAN EMPIRE

ROME EXPANDS

Multiple choice (underline the correct answer).

1. The Greek tyrant Antiochus Epiphanes was forced out of Egypt in 168 B.C.E. by

    a. the Maccabees
    b. Raamses
    c. Pompey

2. Caesar governed Rome

    a. harshly
    b. humanely
    c. indifferently

3. Caesar

    a. forbade Judaism
    b. allowed Jews freedom of worship
    c. confiscated Jewish property

4. The Roman Republic ended and the Roman Empire began in 27 B.C.E. under

    a. Augustus
    b. Julius Caesar
    c. Herod

NATURE OF THE EMPIRE

Two of the statements below are *incorrect*. Find them and identify them by circling the number next to each one.

1. Rome was geared to military life.

2. The Roman Empire provided the Mediterranean countries with notoriously inefficient governments.

3. For entertainment, the Romans loved to watch bloody massacres at the Colosseum.

4. Roman concepts of justice are the foundation for the legal systems of many modern governments.

5. The Pax Romana was a period of relative peace and order.

6. Jewish religious traditions gathered strength and form during the period of the Roman Empire.

7. Among the Empire's many problems after 200 C.E. were inflation, political assassinations, and pressure from Germanic tribes.

8. Despite these problems, the Roman government somehow managed to hang on to its territories.

CHRISTIANITY EMERGES IN THE EAST

1. Who was Constantine and what important religious step did he take?

2. Early Christians were persecuted by the emperors. After Christianity became the official state religion, what happened to the official state attitude toward Jews?

3. What name was given to the Christian religious leader of the city of Rome?

A BIBLICAL CROSSWORD PUZZLE

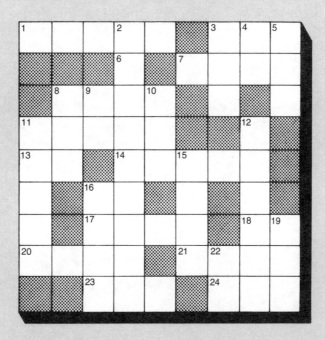

Across

1. Land of Pharaohs
3. Before Common Era
6. article
7. Israel
8. past tense of fall
11. Roman name for Judah
13. Abraham's home town
14. Arab nation
16. pronoun
17. day (Latin)
18. because
20. author of "Understanding Israel"
21. Isaac's eldest son
23. allow
24. _____ God (monotheism)

Down

2. Holy Land
3. large
4. company (abbreviation)
5. finish
8. animal hair
9. editor (abbreviation)
10. set down
11. one of the shoftim
12. Promised Land
15. conquerer of Greece
16. pagan god
19. short for Susan
22. _____ be it

THE MANY NAMES OF THE PROMISED LAND

The land that is now the State of Israel has had many names. Can you remember six other names which have been used to refer to the territory or its parts?

1.

2.

3.

4.

5.

6.

Chapter 6

THE EMERGING TRADITION

JUDEAN CONQUEST

In Chapter 4 we left the Maccabees triumphant in Jerusalem. Jews were in control of Judea. In Chapter 6 we learn how power corrupted the victors and whetted their appetite for conquest. **Fill in the blanks from the words below**.

The royal family of Judea, the _____, ruled for

_____ years. Under the leadership of _____

_____, they conquered _____, forcing every person

there to convert to _____. Only during the reign of the pious

Queen _____ was Judea free of civil strife. But after her death, when her two sons began to quarrel over the throne, Judea

was seized by _____. This happened in the year

_____ _____. At this time in history, one out of

every _____ Romans in the Empire was Jewish.

100	Greece	Idumea	Judah Maccabee
20	Judaism	Salome Alexandra	Herod
27 B.C.E.	ten	Pompey	John Hyrcanus
63 B.C.E.	Syria	Hasmoneans	Judea

HEROD'S REIGN OF TERROR

The Romans made Herod—who came from an Idumean family—King of Judea. **Mark the following true or false.**   (T) (F)

1. Herod's loyalty was to Judea first and to Rome second.   T   F

2. The Idumeans, who had been forced to convert to Judaism, became Herod's staunch supporters.   T   F

3. Herod rebuilt the Jerusalem Temple mainly so that Jews could worship in it once more.   T   F

4. Herod ordered the burning of Jewish patriots who tried to remove a large golden eagle he had placed on the Temple gate. T   F

5. Herod built fortresses partly to use as a refuge against a possible Jewish revolt.   T   F

BE AN EXPERT

If you skipped nothing in this chapter, you are now in command of some important facts about the Dead Sea Scrolls. **Show what you know by underlining the correct word or words.**

1. Where were the Dead Sea Scrolls found? (Tel Aviv) (Qumran caves) (Rome)

2. When were they found? (1947) (1900) (1200)

3. What do they contain? (Biblical texts and commentaries) (the history of the ancient Jews)

4. About how old are they? (1500 years) (2000 years) (3500 years)

5. Who is believed to have written them? (Sadducees) (Essenes) (Greeks)

FACTIONS IN JUDEA

Under Roman rule, the Judeans broke into religious and political factions. **Name the faction described in each paragraph**. (Finding the pun in each description will make this more fun.)

1. They were called Sicarii (dagger men) because they stabbed people in the streets. No Jew who opposed them was safe from these extremists, whose aim was to expel the Romans from Judea. Most Jews saw them as *a lot* of trouble. They were _____.

2. They gave up on society instead of trying to reform it. They withdrew into monklike groups dedicated to prayer, work, and purification in the search for God. You could say they sought the very *essence* of spiritual life. They were _____.

3. These Jews had a good life under the Romans. Thus, it is *sad to see* that they formed a political party designed to preserve their own special privileges. "Let's not rock the boat," they said. In religion, they believed the old ways were the best ways. They were

_____.

4. They were the largest of the factions. They preserved or introduced Jewish traditions that have survived to this day. As *far as* as one can *see*, they were pious and humane in their dedication to Jewish law. They were _____.

THE TEACHERS

| Shemaia | Avtalion | Hillel | Shammai |

Who said it? In the blank spaces, place the name of the teacher or teachers who said, or might have said, the following:

"My teachers have become the most important things in my life. Perhaps they would be angry at me if they knew I was sitting up here on their roof listening to the lesson today because I have no money to pay for it. The snow and bitter wind are freezing me to the marrow, but their words mean more to me than my own comfort."

_____

"Poor man, he is nearly frozen to death. Although the Sabbath is already upon us, we must build a fire to revive him. At a time like this, we have no choice but to break the law." _____

"Idiot! Don't try to make a fool of me. Learn your pagan nonsense standing on one foot. But leave this place at once!" _____

"What is hateful to you, do not do to your neighbor. That is the whole Torah, the rest is commentary." _____

Chapter 7

THE LAST DAYS OF THE TEMPLE

HISTORY MAKERS OF THE ROMAN PERIOD

Match the person with his description by placing the numbers in the appropriate spaces in the second column.

1. Paul
2. Vespasian
3. Josephus
4. Jesus
5. Pontius Pilate
6. Florus
7. Titus

Procurator of Judea who massacred thousands of Jews when they rebelled against his demands for gold from the Temple treasury.

_____

Jewish commander who went over to the enemy. He wrote *The Jewish War*, a sympathetic history of the rebellion against Rome.

_____

He wrote that Jesus ruled in heaven. If not for him, Jesus might have been forgotten.

_____

This emperor came after Nero. He celebrated victory over Jewish rebels by issuing coins inscribed "Judea Capta" (Judah Captured).

_____

He was a brutal, bloodthirsty procurator who made Jewish life intolerable. He ordered the death of Jesus. _____

Romans feared that he might lead a Jewish independence movement. _____

Son of the emperor, he placed Jerusualem under seige. _____

JEWS UNDER TYRANNY

Fill in the blanks from the words listed below.

After the death of King _____, cruel and greedy

_____ were appointed to govern _____. One of the

most vicious was _____ _____. He ordered the

execution of _____, a preacher from Nazareth, because he

feared that this man would lead a Jewish rebellion. Another cruel

administrator, _____, helped himself to Temple gold; this

caused riots, which he stopped by a massacre of 3600 people. In

rebellion, the _____ led a war against Emperor

_____, which lasted from _____ to _____.

The province of _____ was defeated when its commander,

_____, abandoned his command. _____ leaders then

fled to Jerusalem, where a civil war broke out among the Jews.

_____, the son of Emperor _____, placed the city

under siege. The Jews fought valiantly for five months, but the

Romans were too powerful. The Temple went up in flames on the

_____ day of the Hebrew month of _____ in the year

_____.

Nero	Titus	procurators	Jerusalem
Pontius Pilate	Jesus	Zealots	Judea
Florus	Josephus	Judea	Av
Vespasian	Galilee	ninth	Zealot
Nazareth	70 C.E.	66 C.E.	73 C.E.
Herod			

THE MESSIAH IDEA

True or false?   (T)   (F)

1. The idea of a Messiah who would appear among the Jews was a
new one that arose because of Roman oppression.   T   F

2. Some Jews became followers of Jesus.　　T　F

3. Jesus wrote part of the New Testament.　　T　F

4. The main concern of New Testament writings was to show that Jesus was the son of God.　　T　F

5. Jesus had the same religious beliefs as the Pharisees.　　T　F

6. For Jews, Jesus' death was proof that he was not the Messiah.　　T　F

YEARS OF CONFLICT

Complete each sentence by underlining the correct phrase.

1. The civil war in Jerusalem was fought by

    a. the Maccabees against the Pharisees.
    b. the Zealots against the Pharisees.

2. The Sanctuary was

    a. sacked and burned by the Romans.
    b. saved from destruction by the Romans.

3. The Western Wall is a

    a. remnant of a Jewish fortification.
    b. remnant of the Temple in Jerusalem.

4. Masada was a

    a. desert fortress.
    b. Jewish village.

5. The Arch of Titus symbolizes

    a. the vanished glory of Rome.
    b. Jewish victory in war.

SOMETHING TO THINK ABOUT

Jews have held many different notions about the kind of person the Messiah would be. Most have agreed, however, that the Messiah would appear when things were at their worst for our people. How has this belief helped Jews in their struggle for survival?

Chapter 8

NEW TIMES, NEW HEROES

A REMARKABLE STORY

Unscramble the scrambled words.

A very old man and great teacher, Johanan ben Zakkai, outwitted the
L Z O E A T S by pretending to be dead, so that he could escape
from the embattled city of R J E S A L E M U. He played a critical
role in saving U D J I A S M by obtaining permission from Emperor
S P V S A I A N E to teach H O T R A in the town of V A Y N E H in
the year 68 C.E. There he opened an academy that became a source
of scholarship and E I J S W H W A L. Students at the academy
became the first A R B I B S.

Combine the circled letters to form two words that stand for the
great Jewish tradition of word-of-mouth learning begun at this school
and fostered by the Rabbis.

___ ___ ___ ___ ___ ___ ___ ___ ___

Use this space as your work area

WHAT YAVNEH BROUGHT TO JUDAISM

All but two of the following statements are accurate. Circle the numbers next to the *inaccurate* ones.

1. The Academy of Yavneh adapted Judaism to meet the changing times.

2. Yavneh was a source of Jewish law.

3. Yavneh became the new capital of the Jewish religion.

4. The first Jewish leaders to be called "rabbis" were students of Ben Zakkai.

5. The Rabbis in the era of Rome spent all their time studying.

6. The Rabbis carefully evaluated questions and settled differences in a democratic way.

7. Yavneh's scholars maintained the traditions of the Zealots.

8. Yavneh replaced priests with rabbis.

DEMOCRACY—A JEWISH TRAIT

Briefly tell how the Rabbis fostered the democratic process in resolving their differences of opinion.

JEWISH HEROES

Rabbi Joshua ben Hananiah   Bar Kochba

Johanan ben Zakkai   Rabbi Akiva

Match these Jewish heroes to the acts or words that made them famous. (Write one of the above names in each blank space.)

1. After his armies freed Jerusalem, he issued coins inscribed "Redemption of Zion" and "Freedom for Israel." _____

2. Under his guidance, scholars reinterpreted the sacred texts to keep up with the changing times. _____

3. He said, "God gave His Torah to mankind, and decreed that we would interpret it for ourselves. The majority decides. _____
_____

4. He said, "If there is no safety for us in the Torah, which is our home, how can we find safety without it?" _____

LEARNING AND CHARITY

Tell what it was like to be a student in the Age of the Rabbis by answering the following.

1. Since few books were available, how did students learn? _____
_____

2. Why were the lessons usually fascinating? _____
_____

3. How did girls learn Jewish traditions? _____
_____

4. What kind of games did Jewish students play? _____

_____

5. How was community charity practiced? _____

_____

KNOW YOUR HISTORY

True or false?   **(T) (F)**

1. The Jewish people rebelled against Emperor Hadrian because he wanted to dedicate the new Temple to King Solomon.   T   F

2. Bar Kochba's forces, although outnumbered, completely destroyed the Roman army.   T   F

3. In ancient times, many Jewish warriors fought as mercenary soldiers for Middle Eastern nations.   T   F

4. Rabbi Akiva, a shepherd who became a great scholar, was also a pacifist.   T   F

5. The Romans enslaved or killed half a million Jews, crippling Jewish life in Palestine.   T   F

6. Judaism was saved by the few Jews who refused to let traditions die even though they knew that Hadrian put Jews to death for practicing their religion.   T   F

Chapter 9

THE RABBIS TRIUMPHANT

DEVELOPMENT OF JEWISH LAW

1. With the help of other Jewish scholars living under Roman rule, Judah ha-Nasi undertook the massive task of editing and organizing Jewish law and tradition into a book. Until then, these rules and precepts, which stemmed from the Torah, had been passed down orally.

What is the name of the monumental work in which Judah ha-Nasi played a leading role? _____

2. When the book was finished, scholars discussed and debated its contents. Discussions of Jewish law and tradition appear in another monumental work prepared by "Babylonian" Jewry in Persia between 200 C.E. and 500 C.E.

What is the monumental work that discusses the application of Jewish law? ~~Torah~~

3. Together, the two works mentioned above comprise the lifeblood of Jewish thought, the Talmud. Thus we can say that ~~Torah~~

plus _____ = Talmud.

THE SPREAD OF LEARNING

True or false?   (T) (F)

1. The "Jerusalem" Gemara is actually more important than the "Babylonian" Gemara.   (T) (F)

2. Babylonian scholarship became possible after Abba and Samuel returned to Persia from their studies in Palestine. (T) F

3. The Mishnah of the Babylonian Talmud was the ultimate result of the work of Abba and Samuel. (T) F

4. Abba (the Rav) was regarded as a greater scholar than Samuel, although Samuel was both a prominent scholar and a scientist. T (F)

5. Abba created a new academy at Sura which became an intellectual center for world Jewry. (T) F

WORDS THAT BEAR WEIGHT

Chapter 9 has many important words, some of which may be new to you. Let's see how well you know them. **Match the numbered words to their meanings by placing the numbers in the appropriate blanks**.

1. Talmud
2. aggadah
3. halachah
4. siddur
5. Pirke Avot
6. Rav

Scholar of the Babylonian Academy. _____ 6. Rav

Means "Learning." Massive work containing Jewish law and interpretations and discussions. 1. Talmud

Prayer book. 4 Siddur

Means "Chapters of the Fathers." This part of the Talmud contains favorite teachings of the Rabbis as well as stories and legends about them. 5 Pirke Avot

Rabbinical discussions of legal material in the Talmud. Means "the rule to go by." 3 halachah

Rabbinical discussions of Talmudic material. Includes sayings, stories, and legends. Means "to tell."_____

sponge

funnel

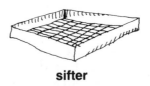
sifter

strainer

According to Pirke Avot, these represent four kinds of students. Which kind are you? Why?

VALUES TAUGHT BY THE RABBIS

Multiple choice (underline the correct answer).

1. With regard to criminal justice, the Rabbis believed in

    a. capital punishment.
    b. just and merciful sentences.
    c. trial by jury.

2. The Rabbis believed animals should

   a. not be kept as pets
   b. be treated humanely and with consideration.
   c. were unimportant in the order of life.

3. The Rabbis thought of God as

   a. a stern judge.
   b. a loving father and friend.
   c. a distant but watchful lawmaker.

4. In the matter of profit-making, the Rabbis generally agreed that

   a. huge profits were unethical.
   b. the merchant should charge whatever he could.
   c. profit-making was not of rabbinical concern.

5. The Rabbis believed that Judaism should

   a. have an official set of beliefs and doctrines.
   b. have no official set of beliefs and doctrines.
   c. be a fixed creed.

6. As for non-Jews, the Rabbis

   a. believed they had a right to worship as they chose and were
      equal in God's eyes.
   b. taught that God would not love them.
   c. believed they would some day see that their beliefs were false.

Chapter 10

THE EMPIRE OF ISLAM

BIRTH OF A NEW RELIGION

Fill in the blanks from the words listed below.

The _____ century saw the birth of a new religion,

_____. The founder of this faith was Muhammad, who was

born in the year _____, in the city of _____. An

uneducated _____ _____, he traveled widely.
During these travels, he learned of two great religions,

_____ and _____. He began to see himself as the

prophet of a new religion whose god was named _____. In

the city of _____ he became an influential political and

religious leader. He tried to convert the _____, but when

these efforts failed, he concentrated on his fellow _____.

Later, many Jews lost their lives when he began a _____

_____ to force his faith on non-believers. In the centuries

that followed, however, Jews and _____, as his followers are
known, worked and learned from each other.

holy war	Muslims	camel driver
Islam	Judaism	Baghdad
seventh	Mecca	
Medina	570 C.E.	
Christianity	Buddhism	
Arabia	Allah	
Jews	Arabs	

THE TEACHINGS OF MUHAMMAD

True or false? (T) (F)

1. The bible of Islam, the Koran, was written before Muhammad's death.   T   F

2. Muhammad taught that all men were equal in the Lord's eyes. T   F

3. He believed that rich people had a right to hang on to their wealth.   T   F

4. He taught that each person would be judged in the hereafter. T   F

5. Muhammad believed in humane treatment of prisoners. T   F

6. He taught that soldiers who died while fighting for Islam would enter Paradise.   T   F

7. Muslims have always prayed facing Jerusalem.   T   F

8. Islam had a revolutionary effect on the Arab world because it introduced monotheism to Arabs.   T   F

THINK ABOUT IT

Imagine yourself a Jew in Muhammad's time. An Arab convert to the new faith of Islam is trying to convince you to follow his example. He argues that Muhammad is the greatest of the prophets. Furthermore, he insists that Islam and Judaism have a

lot in common, mainly the belief in One God. What reasons do you give him for choosing to remain Jewish?

Chapter 11

UNDER ISLAM

JUDAISM FLOURISHES

Jewish scholarship and creativity flourished under tolerant Muslim rule. **Fill in the blanks to complete the descriptions of some Jewish achievements during the seventh and eighth centuries.**

1. Vowels and punctuation were added to ancient Hebrew. The standard Hebrew Bible was established through the study of many different versions prepared by scribes over the centuries. The new standard version became known as the _____ text.

2. For the first time since the Roman Emperor Hadrian recaptured the city, Jews were allowed to live in _____.

3. Jewish communities thrived and became great centers of learning in parts of North _____.

4. The four centuries between 600 and 1000 C.E. when Jewish scholarship flourished under Muslim rule are known as the _____ Period.

WORDS OF WISDOM

Unscramble the scrambled words.

If you were a Jewish scholar living in Eretz I Y S A R E L during the eighth century and were troubled over an interpretation of law, you

44

might write to one of the (E)N I G O M in A Y A B B(I)N L O for help. He would give your questions long and careful consideration, consulting with other scholars if need be. Then he would reply to you in writing, with E P O R S S(N)(A). If you were a C(R)S I B E you would be involved in the massive task of writing the M R A O S A, the standard version of the Hebrew Bible. If you were a scholar in Cairo writing about God, your papers might have been stored in a E(N)I A(G)Z H.

The circled letters form an eight-letter word which is something Jews have always loved and respected. The word is

___ ___ ___ ___ ___ ___ ___ ___

Use this as your work area

A RELIGIOUS CONFLICT

Multiple choice (underline the correct answer).

1. Jewish unity was threatened by the appearance of a religious sect called the

   a. Khazars
   b. Marranos
   c. Karaites

2. This sect rejected the Talmud because

   a. its members were not scholars.
   b. they wanted to create new interpretations of the Bible.
   c. they believed the Rabbis had distorted God's Law.

3. Saadia, the greatest of the Geonim, opposed the movement because

   a. he wanted sole authority.
   b. he believed the sect's interpretation of the Torah was too rigid.
   c. he thought that religious disputes endangered Jewish unity.

4. What great work by Saadia is quoted in the text?

   a. Mishneh Torah
   b. Book of Beliefs and Doctrines
   c. Ode to Zion

5. After Saadia effectively attacked their beliefs, the sect

   a. died out altogether.
   b. started a civil war.
   c. continued to exist but lost its power.

JEWS OF SPAIN

All but two of the following statements are correct. Circle the numbers next to the *incorrect* statements.

1. Before the Muslims invaded Spain in the year 711, Jews suffered violent persecution there at the hands of the Visigoths.

2. Spanish Jews opposed the Muslim invasion.

3. The Muslims placed Jews in control of important Spanish cities.

4. Jews won fame in the professions during an era of toleration that began when Spain became an independent Muslim state in the year 756.

5. There were few restrictions on the practice of the Jewish religion in Spain under Muslim rule.

6. Special taxes and regulations placed on Jews prevented them from attaining the good things in life.

7. Fine scholarly books and volumes of Hebrew poetry were written in the Golden age under Muslim Spanish rule.

SOMETHING TO THINK ABOUT

Jewish art and culture reached extraordinary heights during the Islamic period. What made this possible?

Chapter 12

SOME MEN OF THE GOLDEN AGE

JEWISH SCHOLARSHIP IN SPAIN

Many Jews rose to fame in Spain during the Golden Age. Some of the most prominent are mentioned in this chapter. **Match the name by number to the appropriate description**.

1. Solomon ibn Gabirol
2. Moses Maimonides
3. Judah ha-Levi
4. Samuel ibn Nagrela
5. Ḥasdai ibn Shaprut

Doctor-diplomat who established Jewish schools in Spain. In 950 he became the first Spanish Jew to rise to top rank in government. _____

Scholar-poet who became grand vizier of Granada and military hero. Headed the Jewish community and had a deep attachment to Israel. _____

Ailing, ill-tempered philosopher-poet whose works served as a model for later Jewish poets. Wrote poems used in the High Holy Day service. _____

Physician-poet from Toledo who wrote *Ode to Zion and Kuzari*. _____

Brilliant physician-philosopher, also called RAMBAM. Born in Spain but became famous as the leader of Egyptian Jewry. Wrote *Mishneh Torah* and *Guide to the Perplexed*. _____

FORMING JEWISH VALUES

1. The Golden Age produced many great Jewish scientist-scholars. This is hardly surprising, considering how rigorous the academic program was for boys. If you were a boy who went to a Jewish school in a major Spanish city, what are some of the subjects you would

have studied? _____

_____

_____

_____

2. Judah ibn Tibbon left an "Ethical Will" to his son in which he instructed him in Jewish values. You will recall that he advised his son to give more time to Torah than to the study of medicine, although he wished him to learn both. In your opinion, why did he say

this? _____

_____

_____

_____

DEVELOPMENTS IN THE GOLDEN AGE

Underline the words in parentheses that make each statement correct.

1. The spread of Jewish studies in Spain made Spanish Jews (more) (less) dependent on the Geonim in Babylonia.

2. The Khazars ruled a state where Judaism was the official religion, in what is now (Russia) (Hungary).

3. The most important Jewish community in Spain developed in the city of (Barcelona) (Toledo).

4. The murder of the inept Jewish governor of Granada, Joseph ibn Nagrela, triggered a massacre of (Arabs) (Jews).

Chapter 13

CHRISTIAN EUROPE DURING THE GOLDEN AGE

THE DARK AGES

Fill in the blanks from the words listed below.

After the fall of the _____ Empire, scholarship, culture, and commerce flourished in the _____ world, while ignorance and primitive conditions prevailed in _____ _____.
This period in European history, often called the Dark Ages, lasted from about _____ to _____ C.E. It was a time of turmoil when _____ tribes fought each other and the _____ Church. The king of the Franks, _____, did try to improve education. He founded the _____ _____ _____, which included much of Italy, Germany, France, and _____ _____. After he died, his empire was attacked by _____ from _____.

Christian	France	200	800
Roman	Charlemagne	education	Italy
Germanic	Holy Roman Empire	Vikings	Western Europe
Muslim	Scandinavia	500	Eastern Europe
1000	Belgium	Slavs	plagues

JEWS IN CHRISTIAN EUROPE

One of the answers to each of the following questions is untrue.

Circle the letter next to the *false* statement.

1. What factors helped Jews become successful international tradesmen?

    a. Jews were educated.
    b. Jews were middlemen between Christians and Muslims.
    c. Jewish banks controlled most of Europe's money.
    d. Jews had connections with Jews in distant places.

2. Why did Mainz and Regensburg contain large Jewish settlements?

    a. Because they had large synagogues.
    b. Because they were on trade routes.

3. Who were the Kalonymos?

    a. A Muslim sect.
    b. A Jewish family.
    c. Rabbis, scholars, and community leaders.

HOW JEWS FARED IN BOTH WORLDS

True or false?   (T) (F)

1. Jews were freer from persecution in Muslim lands than in Christian lands.   T F

2. Jews often had Christian servants in medieval Europe.   T F

3. Muslims did not allow Jews to command troops.   T F

4. Jews had complete social equality in the Muslim world.   T F

5. The power of the Christian Church to oppress Jews had no counterpart in Muslim life.   T F

MAP STUDY

Circle the name of a kingdom and the names of cities that were important centers of Jewish life in the year 900 C.E.

ASHKENAZIC OR SEPHARDIC?

Ashkenazic Jews differed from Sephardic Jews in a number of ways. **Distinguish them by placing an A for Ashkenazim or an S for Sephardim in the blank next to each statement.**

1. Jews who lived in Eastern Europe. _____

2. Jews who lived in Muslim lands. _____

3. Jews who lived in Germany. _____

4. Jews who lived in Spain. _____

5. A wordly people, they had limited time for Jewish studies. _____

6. They were deep into Jewish studies and saw the secular world as inferior. _____

7. They produced great scientists, physicians, and statesmen. _____

52

8. Although their communities were small, they maintained a strong Jewish identity. _____

9. They worshipped without a head covering. _____

10. They often kept their heads covered, following the Babylonian practice. _____

THE WISE RABBENU

Imagine you were the great Ashkenazic teacher Rabbenu Gershom. How would you have answered the following question?

"Dear Rabbenu. Last year I was forced to convert to Christianity to save my life. But I can no longer bear to go on living as a Christian. I wish to return to my faith. Will I be condemned forever by my fellow Jews?"

A RENOWNED PERSONALITY

He grew wine grapes and nurtured Jewish minds in Troyes, France, where he started a school in which he taught brilliantly. His commentaries on the Bible and the Talmud were remarkably clear and simple, and he included many midrashim (stories) to illustrate the wisdom of the Torah. His full name was Rabbi Shlomo ben Isaac, but we know him better as _____.

Chapter 14

MIDDLE AGES AND RENAISSANCE

FROM IGNORANCE TO HIGH CULTURE

Fill in the blanks from the words listed below.

The Dark Ages were followed by the period known as the
_____ _____ _____, which lasted from

about _____ to _____ C.E. As _____ spread,

modern _____ took form. Warring _____ seized

control of large areas of land which then became _____. This

was the era of _____. It was also an era of bloody savagery:

_____ _____ was a common practice. While the

nobility lived lavishly in huge _____, ignorance, poverty,
and disease prevailed among the plain people. This era was

followed by the _____, a time of great cultural

achievements, which lasted roughly from _____ to

_____. The most influential and powerful force during this

period was the _____ _____ Church.

Roman Catholic	1000
Christianity	1450
kings	castles
High Middle Ages	1520
witch burning	500
Reformation	knighthood
Europe	nations
Renaissance	knights

DOUBLE CROSTIC

Puzzle-doers who read the chapter thoroughly will love doing this puzzle. Try it, even if it looks hard to you. You may be surprised at how well you do. First, fill in the blanks in the vertical list. (The words are all in the text.) Then, transfer the letters, by number, to the corresponding numbers in the blanks below. If you do the puzzle correctly, you will wind up with an important statement about the Middle Ages and the Renaissance. (As you can see, you've been given a head start on the sentence, so good luck!)

Period dating from
500 to 1000 (2 words)

— — — —　— — — —
6　36　29　42　　72　11　66　22

Famous Renaissance
explorer (full name)

— — — — — — — — — — — 　— — — — — — — —
59　58　88　21　93　1　69　80　58　12　79　　26　86　8　32　39　44　48　23

Conquerors of the
Aztecs (16th cent.)

— — — — — — — — —
67　28　43　85　5　81　37　35　93

Meaning of "Renaissance"

— — — — — — —
41　3　44　90　29　62　2

What they used to
do to witches

— — — —
44　87　17　61

Marrano (2 words)

— — — — — —　— — —
13　92　33　82　46　62　　77　53　54

____ ____ Church:
ruling force in
Renaissance Europe
(2 words)

— — — — —　— — — — — — — —
52　30　4　74　64　　47　14　68　55　78　89　84　57

Masterwork painted
by Michelangelo
(2 words)

— — — — — — —　— — — — — —
22　56　13　50　90　19　38　　47　2　10　70　34　49

Latin word for "Middle Ages" (2 words)

‾ ‾ ‾‾ ‾‾ ‾‾ ‾‾   ‾‾ ‾‾ ‾‾ ‾‾ ‾‾
4 9 31 63 51 75   76 18 91 65 39

Where the Renaissance began (2 words)

‾ ‾‾   ‾‾ ‾‾ ‾‾ ‾‾ ‾‾
5 25   56 83 24 45 73

____ Vinci: Italian artist/scientist (2 words)

‾‾ ‾‾ ‾‾ ‾‾ ‾‾ ‾‾ ‾ ‾‾   ‾‾ ‾‾
71 27 60 15 40 82 7 86   16 20

T H E   M I D D L E   A G E S   A N D   R E N A I S S A N C E
‾ ‾ ‾   ‾ ‾ ‾ ‾ ‾ ‾   ‾‾ ‾‾ ‾‾ ‾‾   ‾‾ ‾‾ ‾‾   ‾‾ ‾‾ ‾‾ ‾‾ ‾‾ ‾‾ ‾‾ ‾‾ ‾‾ ‾‾ ‾‾
1 2 3   4 5 6 7 8 9   10 11 12 13   14 15 16   17 18 19 20 21 22 23 24 25 26 27

P R O D U C E D
‾‾ ‾‾ ‾‾ ‾‾ ‾‾ ‾‾ ‾‾ ‾‾   ‾‾   ‾‾ ‾‾ ‾‾ ‾‾ ‾‾ ‾‾ ‾‾ ‾‾ ‾‾   ‾‾ ‾‾ ‾‾ ‾‾ ‾‾ ‾‾ ‾‾
28 29 30 31 32 33 34 35   36   37 38 39 40 41 42 43 44 45 46   47 48 49 50 51 52 53

‾‾ ‾‾ ‾‾ ‾‾ ‾‾   ‾‾ ‾‾ ‾‾ ‾‾ ‾‾ ‾‾ ‾‾ ‾‾ ‾‾   ‾‾ ‾‾   ‾‾ ‾‾ ‾‾ ‾‾   ‾‾
54 55 56 57 58   59 60 61 62 63 64 65 66 67   68 69   70 71 72 73   74

‾‾ ‾‾ ‾‾ ‾‾ ‾‾   ‾‾ ‾‾ ‾‾ ‾‾   ‾‾ ‾‾   ‾‾ ‾‾ ‾‾   ‾‾ ‾‾ ‾‾ ‾‾ ‾‾
75 76 77 78 79   80 81 82 83   84 85   86 87 88   89 90 91 92 93

Chapter 15

CATHOLIC EUROPE VERSUS THE JEWS

Anti-Semitism spread through Christian Europe during the High Middle Ages and Renaissance. This chapter gives a general view of how the Jews became the object of officially sanctioned persecution.

THE CRUSADES

Multiple choice (underline the correct answer).

1. The main source of attacks against Jews was

   a. the Roman Catholic Church.
   b. medieval kings.
   c. rival tradesmen.

2. The stated purpose of the First Crusade was to

   a. dramatize Christianity's appeal.
   b. free the Holy Land from Muslim control.
   c. convert non-Christians.

3. The first Crusade began in the year

   a. 1000.
   b. 1101.
   c. 1096.

4. To Pope Urban II, the Crusade was

   a. a way to show his religious leadership.
   b. a display of pageantry.
   c. a way to wipe out his enemies.

5. To nobles, the Crusades promised

    a. a chance to mobilize their knights.
    b. possibilities for wealth and adventure.
    c. a way to meet Muslim leaders.

6. To Italian merchants, the Crusades offered a way to

    a. unblock trade routes.
    b. obtain the Pope's favor.
    c. sell merchandise to the Vikings.

CHRISTIANITY ON THE ATTACK

Rhineland massacres

Destruction of Jerusalem (1099)

Blood Libel

Desecrating the Host

Scapegoats for disasters

Anti-Jewish laws

Disputations

Book burnings

Job discrimination

"Shylock" stereotype

Define:

1. Blood Libel _____

_____

_____

2. Desecrating the Host _____
_____
_____

3. Scapegoat _____
_____
_____

4. Disputation _____
_____
_____

WHO IS THIS MAN OF VALOR?

He was a Spanish physician and Talmudic scholar who spoke up for Jewish rights at the Disputation of Barcelona. Exiled from Spain, he traveled to Eretz Yisrael. His letter from Jerusalem told how he helped a handful of Jews make plans to rebuild the synagogue—even though the city's surviving Jewish population consisted of only two Jews!

His name is N ____ ____ ____ ____ ____ ____ ____ ____ s.

Chapter 16

IN THE LANDS OF WESTERN EUROPE

TOLERATION IN ITALY

In the 1200's, Italy tolerated Jews for a variety of reasons. **Circle the letter before the reason that is *least* likely to be valid.**

a.   A unified anti-Jewish policy was not possible because Italy was divided up into independent rival territories.

b.   Southern Italy was in touch with the Muslim world, where Jews were well treated.

c.   Northern city-states in need of money were hospitable to Jewish moneylenders.

d.   Some of the Popes spoke out against anti-Jewish violence.

e.   Many Jews looked like Italians.

f.   The Italian people had little liking for religious oppression.

THE GERMAN "MERRY-GO-ROUND"

For Jews in medieval German-speaking lands, life was "a sad merry-go-round" because they were forced to move from one territory to another. Explain why and how this happened. _____

_____

_____

_____

_____

THE RISE AND FALL OF ENGLISH JEWRY

Multiple choice (underline the correct answer).

1. The first Jews entered England

    a. after the Norman conquest.
    b. during the reign of Richard the Lion-Hearted.
    c. during the reign of Edward I.

2. During the Middle Ages, Jews in England served the Christian world mainly as

    a. peddlers.
    b. scribes.
    c. moneylenders.

3. The Blood Libel led to many anti-Jewish riots. In 1189, mobs ignored an order by King Richard I protecting the Jews. The worst violence was the massacre of Jews in

    a. London.
    b. York.
    c. Bath.

4. Jews lost all protection in England when

    a. Christian moneylenders arrived from Italy.
    b. Jews refused to lend money.
    c. Jews withheld their taxes.

5. All Jews were expelled from England in 1290 during the reign of

    a. William the Conqueror.
    b. King Richard I.
    c. King Edward I.

6. After expulsion, Jews were not allowed to enter England for

    a. 350 years.
    b. 50 years.
    c. 150 years.

PERSECUTIONS IN FRANCE

1. What was so special about Provence in the early Middle Ages, as far as Jews were concerned? _____

_____

_____

2. What happened to the Jews of Provence when Pope Innocent III launched a crusade against Christian heretics? _____

_____

_____

3. Between 1182 and 1322, France expelled Jews five times and then recalled them. Why were they recalled? _____

_____

_____

4. In 1394, Jews were again banished from France. How long did this ban last? _____

_____

_____

5. The crudely drawn figure on page 139 of the text, from a French law code, is a Jew. What did this law require him to do to identify himself as different from non-Jews? _____

_____

_____

THE SPANISH TRAGEDY

In 1391, 50,000 Jews were killed and another 100,000 were forced to convert to Christianity within a few months. Suppose one of these Spanish converts smuggled this letter to a relative in another country:

Dear Cousin Avrom,

Word may have reached you somehow that I have abandoned our faith and converted to Roman Catholicism. Alas, the news is all too true. I was given the choice of insufferable persecution for myself and my dear Anna and the children, or baptism into Christianity. I bear the burden of my choice with a heavy heart, although as a "New Christian" many doors have been opened to me and I now have a high post in government. Many former Jews pretend devotion to Christianity but secretly remain true to the Jewish faith, carrying out the ancient rituals and customs behind drawn curtains. I tremble for our fate should the authorities discover this. More I dare not write. Be assured that we remain in good health and uncrushed in spirit.

Your devoted kinsman,
Isaac

Complete the sentences that follow with words that have the same meaning as those listed below.

1. Had Avrom read between the lines, he would have guessed that Isaac had become a _____.

2. Had Isaac been alive in 1478 his fears would have been even greater, because in that year the Catholic Church began to punish secret Jews through the _____.

3. Punishment was usually made into a public spectacle, which the Spanish religious authorities called an _____.

4. Had Isaac been a Jew in 1492 he would have been forced to leave Spain by an order proposed by _____.

    1. secret Jew   3. "act of faith"
    2. ecclesiastical court   4. the Grand Inquisitor

64

THE INQUISITION AT WORK

The horrifying power of the Inquisition is shown in the painting on page 119.

1. Who are the two figures strapped to the posts? _____

_____

_____

_____

2. For what crime are they being punished? _____

_____

_____

_____

3. What will happen to them? _____

_____

_____

_____

Chapter 17

JEWISH RESISTANCE

REMAINING JEWISH AT ANY COST

The names and terms in the first column are associated with Jewish survival in the Middle Ages. Match them to their descriptions by placing the correct number in the proper blank.

1. Abraham ibn Ezra
2. Meir of Rothenberg
3. Kabbalists
4. Tzedakah
5. Johannes Reuchlin
6. Kiddush ha-Shem

A mother stabs her two small children to death, then kills herself, because she refuses to profane God's name by accepting the divinity of Jesus. _____

Living in the constant fear of attack by outsiders, the Jewish community takes special care to provide for all of its members. The rich give generously to the poor.

_____

He spends the last 24 years of his life traveling from one country to another to bring Jews learning and hope, thereby helping them resist Christian pressures.

_____

This old German rabbi tries but fails in an attempt to lead Jews to the Holy Land. Imprisoned for seven years, he refuses to be ransomed by his fellow Jews.

_____

A renowned Christian scholar, he defends Judaism in a dispute with a Jewish convert to Catholicism, Johannes Pfefferkorn.

_____

These devout scholars try to protect the Jewish community through mysticism. They devoted themselves to prayer, meditation, and a search for hidden meanings in Torah. _____

True or false? **(T)** **(F)**

1. Despite the threat of torture and other persecutions, most Jews in medieval Europe stood by their religion.   T   F

2. It was easy for Jews to escape from lands where they were persecuted.   T   F

3. Sometimes Jews were forbidden to escape because their skill in business gave them value to Christian rulers.   T   F

4. The medieval Jew's strongest weapon of resistance was Jewish practice.   T   F

5. In 1096 the Jews of Mainz saved themselves from the Crusaders by bribing the bishop to give them sanctuary.   T   F

6. Captured Jews were forced to say that Jesus was the son of God.   T   F

KABBALAH

Unscramble the scrambled words. Form the name of the work

described in the following paragraph by combining the five circled letters.

The (A)B A L K B S I T S worked with E A (Z) L to convince medieval E W J S that this work was a sacred text and a powerful source of M (O) F C O T R. Its E (H) T M E is that man's righteous acts bring God's presence into the N I E (R) U V S E. This work is called the

___ ___ ___ ___ ___

Most scholars today believe this work was written in the late thirteenth century by (check one)

    a. Simeon ben Yohai
    b. Moses de Leon

Use this as your work area

EDUCATION AMONG THE ASHKENAZIM

1. If you were a boy in a Jewish community in medieval times, you would, like your father, spend a lot of time in the synagogue. What functions would the synagogue perform for you and your community? _____

_____

_____

2. If you were an Ashkenazic woman in medieval times, what would

be your religious role? ———————————————————————

In addition to homemaking, what other role might you play in family

affairs? ———————————————————————————————

———————————————————————————————————

———————————————————————————————————

SOMETHING TO THINK ABOUT

Observance of Jewish customs and ceremonies gives Jewish life variety, interest, and meaning today as it did in medieval times. Tradition is a source of strength and security. In your own words, tell why this is so.

Chapter 18

REFORMATION AND ENLIGHTENMENT

CHRISTIANITY SPLITS

Fill in the blanks, from the words listed below.

Angered by abuses by the Roman Catholic Church, a German monk named _____ _____ broke away from Catholicism, a break which led to the _____ _____. As a result, many _____ states declared themselves independent of the _____ _____ _____ as _____ spread among them. The Church of Rome, in trouble, began to reform itself in a movement called the _____. The appearance of many _____ sects ushered in a new era of religious _____ and wars. The worst war, starting in the year _____, was known as the _____ _____ _____. The treaty that ended this war in _____ allowed the coexistence of many forms of _____ by allowing kings or princes to select each country's religion. While Christian Europeans then became relatively _____ among themselves, they did not extend this attitude toward Jews, who by this time were isolated in

_____.

Roman Catholic Church	German	tolerant
intolerance	Counter-Reformation	Martin Luther
Christianity	Thirty Years' War	1521
Protestant Reformation	Christian	1648
1618	ghettos	Protestantism

A CHANGING WORLD

Complete the sentences.

1. Protestant followers of Martin Luther became known as ———
—————————.

2. Reason took a back seat when the Inquisition put Galileo on trial in 1633 for demonstrating that the earth revolves around the
—————————.

3. The list of books banned by the Catholic Church is known as the
————————— ————————— ————————— —————————.

4. Scientific inquiry weakened the power of such kings as Louis IV who claimed to rule by ————————— —————————.

ENLIGHTENMENT

True or false?   (T) (F)

1. Science was regarded as the key to knowledge in the era known as the "Age of Reason" or "Enlightenment."   T F

2. The Jewish people played a direct role in making Christians more tolerant.   T F

3. Christian intellectuals in Europe learned through science that kings had a hereditary right to their power.   T F

4. Judaism taught ideas embodied in the Declaration of Independence thousands of years before such Enlightenment scholars as Thomas Jefferson expressed them.   T F

Chapter 19

THE SIXTEENTH CENTURY — IN ISOLATION

THE GHETTO SYSTEM

Confinement to the ghetto brought hardship to Jews, but also a few benefits. **Find the *benefits* among the burdens of ghetto life on the following list and circle the number next to them.**

1. isolation
2. overcrowding
3. unhealthy conditions
4. close-knit community life
5. heavy taxation
6. synagogues within walking distance
7. pressures to convert
8. poverty
9. stifling of intellectual life
10. disease
11. protection from mob attacks
12. freedom to practice rituals and customs
13. anti-Jewish laws
14. Jewish badges

CREATORS AND CREATIONS

Match the name to the description. Place the number next to each name in the appropriate blank.

1. Leo da Modena
2. Judah Loew

Prague chief rabbi, scholar, and writer.

_____

3. Golem
4. Joseph Karo
5. Gluekel of Hameln
6. Shulchan Aruch

Ghetto cultural leader in Venice known even among non-Jews for his sermons.
_____

Author of detailed instructions for the conduct of Jewish life. _____

Imaginary robot-like creature. _____

"Prepared Table"—a work of instructions on Jewish living. _____

Jewish woman who wrote a detailed record of German-Jewish life. _____

CUSTOM AND TRADITION

1. Chicken soup again? Explain the origin of the Shabbat custom.
_____
_____

2. Helm was always good for a laugh among ghetto folk. Why? ___

_____
_____

3. "Es ist shver tzu sine a Yid" is an old Yiddish complaint meaning, "It is hard (heavy) to be a Jew." But oppression and adversity failed to extinguish the zest for living of European ghetto Jews. How did they entertain themselves? _____

_____
_____

4. How did the development of Yiddish affect the relationship of

Eastern Jewry to the Gentile world? _____

_____

_____

YIDDISH

True or false?   (T) (F)

1. Ashkenazic Jews created Yiddish.   T   F

2. Yiddish developed in Poland.   T   F

3. Yiddish is a combination of German, Slavic, and Hebrew words.   T   F

4. Yiddish is written in the Hebrew alphabet.   T   F

5. Yiddish is too limited for literary use.   T   F

JEWS OF PRAGUE AND ROME

Complete each statement.

1. The Prague ghetto was distinguished for its scholarship, size, and—at first—relative security. Like other Jewish communities, in

time it suffered _____

_____

_____.

2. Among the many oppressive laws directed against the Jewish people of Rome was one that turned them into ragpickers. This law

stated that _____

_____

_____.

3. The homes of Roman Jews were always in jeopardy. Every year until 1850, Jews had to formally beg for _____

_____

_____.

Chapter 20

LANDS OF HOPE

A "LITTLE GOLDEN AGE"

Multiple choice (underline the correct answer).

1. The Ottoman Empire offered a haven to Spanish and Portuguese Jewish refugees in

    a. Montenegro and Cyprus.
    b. Poland, Hungary, and Austria.
    c. Turkey, North Africa, and Palestine.

2. Turkish Jews reached a "Golden Age" by

    a. the middle of the sixteenth century.
    b. the end of the fifteenth century.
    c. the year 1601.

3. After gaining control of Palestine by 1517, the Turks

    a. limited Jewish immigration.
    b. revived the economy by bringing in Jewish immigrants.
    c. drove out local populations.

4. The largest and most important Jewish community in Palestine during the seventeenth century was

    a. Safed.
    b. Tiberias.
    c. Jerusalem.

5. Oppression of Jews during Ottoman rule

a. was outlawed.
b. happened on occasion.
c. never occurred.

6. When the Ottoman Empire began to decline in the late 1600's,

    a. Jews fled to the New World.
    b. the quality of Jewish life in Turkey declined.
    c. Jews were driven from Turkey.

7. History shows that during most of the sixteenth century, Turkish Muslims were

    a. helpful to Jews.
    b. ruled by the Jews.
    c. bitterly anti-Jewish.

THE NETHERLANDS—A SECOND HAVEN

Complete the sentences.

1. The Netherlands was not able to offer sanctuary to Jewish refugees as long as it was ruled by _____.

2. In 1579, the Dutch people revolted following their conversion to _____.

3. The first Jewish immigrants to the Netherlands settled and built a synagogue in the city of _____

4. Holland (the Netherlands) was rewarded economically for its kindness, when Jews built up its _____.

5. The portrait by Rembrandt on page 181 of the text shows the Dutch Jewish leader who led a movement to allow Jews to return to England after 350 years of exile. His name was Rabbi _____.

6. The English leader favored the readmission of Jews to England during the 1650's was a Puritan named _____.

LANDS OF HOPE

Match the names to the descriptions by placing the numbers in the appropriate blank spaces.

1. Turks
2. Ladino
3. Spinoza
4. Safed
5. Gracia Mendes

6. Holland
7. Joseph Nasi
8. Joseph Karo
9. Isaac Luria
10. Marranos

Rich, charitable woman who aided refugees. _____

Sultan's adviser. _____

Mystical rabbi known as ARI. _____

Secret Jews. _____

Author of Shulchan Aruch. _____

Spanish-Hebrew tongue. _____

Land of hope. _____

Philosopher-heretic. _____

Holy Land Jewish town. _____

Sixteenth century friends of Jews. _____

JEWS IN THE NEW WORLD

1. After Columbus discovered America, what happened to Jews who entered those parts of the Western Hemisphere controlled by Spain

and Portugal? _____

_____

_____

2. What nation made it possible for Jews to settle in America?

_____

_____

3. They came by way of Brazil. They fled that country when Holland lost control of Brazil to Portugal. Captured by pirates, they were stranded on a deserted island. There they were picked up by a French ship and brought to New Amsterdam—a tattered, weary group of 23 men, women, and children. Who were they?

_____

_____

Chapter 21

THE SEVENTEENTH CENTURY — MAJOR CENTERS AND MAJOR UPHEAVALS

EASTERN EUROPEAN JEWS

Multiple choice (underline the correct answer).

1. Poland had more Jews than any other nation during the Reformation and Enlightenment periods. In 1640 the Jewish population in Poland was

    a. 15,000.
    b. 250,000.
    c. 500,000.

2. Jews who flocked to Poland in the thirteenth century to escape persecution in Western Europe

    a. were excluded from business in Poland.
    b. became active in every phase of Polish economic life.
    c. were restricted to certain kinds of work in Poland.

3. Polish Jewry became famous for its

    a. high educational standards.
    b. ceremonial dances.
    c. trade in smoked fish.

4. Polish King Boleslav

    a. ordered pogroms against Jews.
    b. founded the town of Ḥelm.
    c. issued a charter to protect Jews from attacks by Christians.

5. Increasingly separated from Christians and hated by them, Polish Jews

    a. concentrated on their own culture, speaking Yiddish among themselves.
    b. tried to adapt to Polish culture.
    c. refused to speak Polish.

6. In Eastern Europe, Jews belonged to "kehillahs," which were

    a. communes.
    b. fraternal organizations.
    c. communities.

7. For over 100 years, Eastern European Jews sent representatives to a governing body called

    a. Jews for Democratic Action.
    b. the Council of the Four Lands.
    c. the Kabbalah.

THE FALSE MESSIAH

Complete the sentences.

1. Few Jews were spared Polish brutality in the decade following 1648. Some escaped to Hungary, Turkey, Germany, or Holland. Others were killed in massacres or enslaved, and many survived by

_____.

2. Jews who remained in Poland expected the Messiah to appear and lead them to _____.

3. In the second half of the sixteenth century, Shabbetai Zevi was able to convince many thousands of Jews that he was the

_____.

4. Shabbetai was arrested and held in a Turkish jail. The Sultan

offered him the choice of _____ or _____.

5. Most of the Jewish world reacted to Shabbetai's choice with _____.

SOMETHING TO THINK ABOUT

Do you believe that Jews should continue to hope for a personal Messiah? Why?

WORD SEARCH

The words in capital letters below are hidden in the diagram that follows. They may appear vertically or horizontally, with their letters in their usual order or backwards. Each time you find one of them, draw a line around it. Some words share a letter, so their circles will be linked.

POLAND had the largest seventeenth century Jewish population. Polish Jewry esteemed **EDUCATION**.
Jewish schools gave students unlimited **OPPORTUNITY**.
Poland's teachers became leaders of European **JEWRY**.
Gentile society favored the **EXCLUSION** of Jews.
Talmudists "peppered" their studies with **PILPUL**.
The Jewish community was called a **KEHILLAH**.
The Governing body of Jews for Eastern Europe was the Council of the **FOUR LANDS**. This council was **DEMOCRATIC**.
COSSACKS launched a wave of violence against Polish Jews in 1648.

O	R	L	B	C	D	P	O	E	R	S	N
P	I	L	P	U	L	O	K	M	K	D	N
P	E	X	O	Y	R	W	E	J	I	N	C
O	X	R	L	K	E	B	H	L	O	A	I
R	C	A	A	M	E	W	I	N	O	L	T
T	L	B	N	V	D	I	L	Y	P	R	A
U	V	C	D	C	G	J	L	F	Q	U	R
N	S	W	T	S	K	C	A	S	S	O	C
I	I	F	R	H	A	L	H	E	G	F	O
T	O	F	S	J	O	P	Q	S	T	B	M
Y	N	X	N	O	I	T	A	C	U	D	E
E	B	C	U	R	X	I	V	U	Z	A	D

Chapter 22

THE EIGHTEENTH CENTURY—MYSTICS AND MODERNS

REACHING GOD THROUGH FEELINGS

The following paragraph describes a Jewish movement that began in the first half of the 1700's. **Unscramble the scrambled words. Then combine the circled letters.** They should spell the name of the man who founded this powerful movement, which turned despair into joy and celebration.

To the O (O) P R and oppressed Jews of Poland, who were
U P E R T T I O I U (S) S S and largely uneducated, a leader appeared
who showed them a new way to relate to God. He said that the
(T) L M (A) G H Y I could be reached through (L) E F N G I S E, and he
taught his followers to express their faith through joyous
A D N C N I G and singing and religious L Z E (A.) He told them that
O (V) L E for God meant more than D U (A) T C N I O E. The
movement is very much alive today and is called I H A D I S M S.
The man who founded it was born R I S L A E   E (B) N
E Z R (E) L I E, but he was known as the

___ ___ ___ ___ ___   ___ ___ ___ ___ ___   ___ ___ ___

Use this as your work area

A ḤASIDIC TALE

Many delightful tales have come out of the Ḥasidic movement, such as the one about the little shepherd boy who talked to God with his flute. Because his family was poor, he could not go to school and had to take care of sheep instead. While he watched his sheep, he played his flute. One Yom Kippur his father took him to the synagogue. The lad felt very downcast as he saw the others reading their prayers, for he did not know how to read. He was almost bursting with longing to speak to the Almighty. Unable to control himself, he took his flute, which he had hidden under his shirt, and began to play it. As the silvery notes rose skyward, everyone else stopped praying, in amazement. Angry and embarrassed, his father was about to seize the flute, when the voice of the rabbi rang out, "Don't be unkind to the lad. In his own way, and with true feeling, he is reaching God—perhaps better than the rest of us!"

How does this story illustrate the philosophy of the Ḥasidim?

_____

_____

_____

_____

THE HASIDIC WAY OF LIFE

1. Why was the Ḥasidic movement so attractive to the poor and uneducated Jews of Poland? _____

_____

_____

2. Why are Ḥasidic males easy to recognize, even today?

_____

_____

_____

3. Describe the role of Zaddikim in Ḥasidic life.

_____

_____

_____

4. Why did Ḥasidic leaders become a source of weakness to the movement? _____

_____

_____

5. What has the Ḥasidic movement contributed to Judaism?

_____

_____

_____

6. Ḥabad evolved in eighteenth century Lithuania as a branch of Ḥasidism. In what way has it differed from the parent movement?

_____

_____

_____

THE OPPOSITION

1. The Council of the Four Lands gave its blessing to the new Ḥasidic movement in Poland. **True or false?** _____

2. Elijah ben Solomon was given the honorary title of Gaon and was widely known as the Vilna Gaon. Where is Vilna? _____ Why was the Vilna Gaon so greatly respected? _____

3. The Vilna Gaon disapproved of Ḥasidism because (*underline the incorrect response*): (a) the movement changed ritual; (b) he believed music was sinful; (c) the movement attacked the valuable Jewish tool of scholarship; (d) the movement encouraged feeling rather than thinking.

4. The Ḥasidic movement and the Mitnagdim eventually came to terms. How did this happen? _____
_____
_____
_____

MOSES MENDELSSOHN

Multiple choice (underline the correct answer or answers).

1. Moses Mendelssohn was

   a. a brilliant scholar who rose from poverty.
   b. a Court Jew.
   c. the author of a German translation of the Bible.

2. As a German Jew, he

   a. flirted with Christianity.
   b. was committed to Judaism and Jewry.
   c. wrote German novels.

3. He believed that

    a. if Jews mastered European culture they would be accepted in German society.
    b. Jews did not have to conform to modern ways.
    c. Hebrew should be the first language of German Jews.

4. His friend, the playwright Gotthold Ephraim Lessing,

    a. remained aloof from the Jewish plight.
    b. modeled a character after him.
    c. was also a spokesman for Jews and religious freedom.

THE COURT JEW

All but one of the following statements about the "Court Jew" are correct. Circle the number next to the *incorrect* statement.

1. He had to keep his prince supplied with money.

2. He bought supplies for the army.

3. He often served as the prince's political adviser.

4. He gained privilege and wealth and sometimes was admitted to the nobility.

5. He was free from many anti-Jewish laws.

6. He earned a permanent place in aristocratic society.

7. He served on diplomatic missions.

THE EIGHTEENTH CENTURY

Match the names in the first column with the corresponding term or description and write the number in the appropriate blank space.

1. Ḥasidism
2. Elijah ben Solomon
3. Joseph Suess
   Oppenheimer
4. Mitnagdim
5. Baal Shem
6. Zaddik
7. Ḥabad
8. Moses Mendelssohn
9. Gotthold Ephraim
   Lessing
10. Martin Buber

Holy man _____

German-Jewish scholar _____

Vilna Gaon _____

Philosopher who wrote on

    Ḥasidism _____

Opponents of Ḥasidism _____
Author of "Nathan the Wise"

_____

"Religion of the pious" _____

Master of the Name _____

Court Jew _____

Branch of Ḥasidism _____

Chapter 23

THE MODERN ERA

THE JEWISH CONTRIBUTION

The picture essay that precedes this chapter gives us a sense of the vitality of Jewish life in various parts of the modern world. The chapter skims developments in the past 200 years and shows how Jews have contributed to and been affected by rapid social changes since 1775. (A second volume will deal with these years in depth.) Test your recall of some of these developments.

1. In his Preface to Part Six, Abba Eban discusses his various roles as a maker of history. In 1949–59, for instance, he was Israel's Ambassador to the United Nations. Why was this role, at this time in Israel's history, of special importance to the new Jewish state?

_____

_____

_____

2. Jews helped fight and finance the American Revolution. Who was Haym Salomon? _____

_____

_____

3. Which nation contains the largest, wealthiest, and most influential Diaspora community? _____

_____

_____

_____

4. Why is the Mikvé Israel synagogue in Curaçao famous?

_____

_____

_____

5. Three men of Jewish birth had a profound impact on modern thought. Write their names in the blank spaces next to their areas of importance.

a. politics—socialism and communism _____

b. physics—theory of relativity _____

c. psychology—psychoanalysis _____

MODERN HISTORY

Fill in the blanks from the words listed on the next page.

The modern period is said to have begun with the _____

_____ in the year _____. It inspired the overthrow

of tyranny and _____ in France and other countries. However, in Eastern Europe, where the largest number of Jews lived, revolutionary outbreaks failed to loosen the tight control held by the _____. The development of science and industry in

the early 1800's led to another kind of revolution, the _____

_____. By giving the common people more power, it helped

the progress of _____. But at the same time, Western

powers in need of new materials and _____ established

_____ in Africa and Asia. In 1914, _____

_____ _____ broke out. As a consequence, the empires of Eastern Europe were broken up, the Communists seized

control of _____, and Germany was left in chaos. During the

great economic _____ of the _____, Adolf Hitler

rose to power. The Western democracies finally realized that Hitler was a threat to all humanity after he invaded _____ in 1939. This set off _____ _____ _____. In the aftermath, the United States and the _____ _____ became the leading world powers. Among other important developments has been the banding together of African, Asian, and South American nations, led by the _____ _____ countries. Known as the _____ _____, these countries have put economic pressure on the industrialized West.

depression	monarchies	Russia
Industrial Revolution	World War II	1930's
democracy	Poland	oil producing
World War I	1775	aristocracy
American Revolution	Third World	colonies
	markets	Soviet Union

Chapter 24

THE JEWS IN MODERN EUROPE

HISTORICAL HIGHLIGHTS

Multiple choice (underline the correct answer).

1. When Napoleon took over France in 1799, he promised to protect the rights of Jewish people in France. In fact, he

   a. granted Jews full equality.
   b. freed Jews from the ghettos in countries he conquered.
   c. appointed Jews to high government positions.

2. After Napoleon's defeat at Waterloo, German and Italian states

   a. continued to respect Jewish rights.
   b. forced Jews to emigrate.
   c. restored anti-Jewish laws.

3. Many German Jews thought they could escape oppression and advance socially by converting to Christianity. Between 1800 and 1810 the percentage of German-Jewish converts was

   a. 10 percent.
   b. 3 percent.
   c. 50 percent.

4. The German-Jewish scholar Leopold Zunz created the "Science of Judaism" in order to

   a. study Jewish racial characteristics.
   b. develop Jewish scientists.
   c. research the Jewish past with modern historical techniques.

5. The first big breakthrough in the field of Jewish biography was

    a. Leopold Zunz's study of Rashi.
    b. Nicholas Halasz' *Captain Dreyfus*.
    c. Jacob Guttermann's *Moses ben Maimon*.

6. Among the many literary and historical studies of Judaism in the nineteenth century, one of the most notable was

    a. Max Dimont's *Jews, God and History*.
    b. Heinrich Graetz's *History of the Jews*.
    c. Cecil Roth's *A Short History of the Jewish People*.

NEW APPROACHES TO JUDAISM

1. Match the branch of Judaism with its doctrine by writing the proper letter in the blank that follows each statement.

a. Reform
b. Orthodox
c. Conservative
d. Reconstruc-
   tionist
e. Neo-Orthodox

Believes that changes should be made slowly and carefully. _____

Stresses ethics rather than rituals and laws; upholds basic Jewish values but also regards each Jew as the final authority for his or her own acts. _____

Believes that Judaism is both a religion and a constantly changing way of life. _____

Believes that only by observing the law as taught in the Torah and interpreted in the Talmud can Jews keep a unique religious identity.

_____

Looks to the Torah for moral authority but is flexible about observance of traditions and accepts the value of a secular culture. _____

2. Match the name in the first column with the movement that is most closely associated with him (write the correct letter in each blank space).

a. Leopold Zunz

b. Abraham Geiger

c. Mordecai Kaplan

d. Theodor Herzl

e. Samson Raphael Hirsch

Neo-Orthodoxy _____

Father of Zionism _____

Reconstructionism _____

Science of Judaism _____

Reform Judaism _____

DREYFUS AND HERZL

"Death to the Jews!" the crowd yelled when they ripped the Captain's stripes from his uniform. . . . If an otherwise progressive, surely highly civilized people could come to such a pass, what was there to be expected from other people?

Fill in the blanks.

1. The man who wrote the above words was Theodor Herzl. Aroused by the prejudice of the French masses, he devoted himself to the idea of a Jewish _____.

2. The army captain he referred to was named _____ _____.

3. The captain's trial took place during the end of the _____ century.

4. He was convicted on false evidence of being a _____.

5. The case attracted international attention because it brought the prevalence of French _____ into the open.

6. Herzl first published his ideas about a Jewish homeland in a document called _____ _____ _____.

7. Herzl called together the first official, worldwide gathering of Jews on August 29, 1897. This meeting was named the _____

_____ _____.

8. Although, as Herzl put it, he "created the Jewish State" in 1897, the State of Israel actually did not come into being until _____.

9. Ironically, the creation of a Jewish homeland was hastened by Hitler's murder of European Jews, in what has come to be known as the _____.

THE RISE OF HITLER

Answer Yes or No.

1. Did the German people as a whole accept Hitler's persecution of the Jews without protest? _____

2. The Nuremberg laws of 1935 stripped Jews of all rights of citizenship, and Hitler destroyed organized German-Jewish life in the brutal *Kristallnacht*. Did the governments of other nations attempt to stop him? _____

3. When homeless German Jews came to seek refuge, did the Western nations open their doors? _____

4. If you were a Jew living in Poland, the Ukraine, or France when Hitler was in power, could you have trusted your non-Jewish countrymen to protect you from the Nazis? _____

5. Did Hitler's "Final Solution" succeed in destroying Jewish life in Germany forever? _____

6. Did the Dutch and Danish people help their Jewish citizens? _____

SOMETHING TO THINK ABOUT

What conditions in modern Europe made it essential for Jews to have a state of their own?

Chapter 25

TODAY'S MAJOR CENTERS

JEWS UNDER COMMUNISM

All but one of the following statements are correct. Circle the number next to the *incorrect* one.

1. Jews were officially declared a separate nationality by the Soviet government.

2. Passports of Russian Jews identify them as Jews rather than Russians.

3. The Communists shut down most synagogues in the Soviet Union.

4. The Communists have not hampered religious education in the U.S.S.R.

5. Jewish emigration from the Soviet Union has been restricted, causing many Jews to live there against their will.

IN THE LAND OF THE CZARS

True or false?   (T) (F)

1. As the principality of Moscow grew and acquired territories, becoming modern Russia, Jews were welcomed as citizens.   T F

2. After Russia conquered Lithuania and Poland in 1772, Jews were confined to areas within the "Pale of Settlement" and suffered endless persecution.   T F

3. At the age of twelve, some Jewish boys in Russia were forced into military service and sent to Siberia. Forced to convert to Christianity, these "Cantonists," as they were called, never rejoined the Jewish faith.   T   F

4. Czar Alexander II showed kindness to Jews in 1855 when he lifted restrictions against them. He had no hidden motive.   T   F

5. Haskalah was a movement of Jews formed during the reign of Czar Alexander II to bring Jews into the mainstream of Russian culture.   T   F

6. Czars instigated "pogroms," mob attacks upon Jews.   T   F

7. The "May Laws," which forced Jews out of rural areas, were designed to turn Jews into well-paid industrial laborers.   T   F

IN AMERICA

1. Which constitutional amendment guaranteed religious freedom in the United States? _____

2. In 1825 there were only 6000 Jews and nine congregations in the United States. What happened in Central Europe in the 1840's to send many thousands of Jews fleeing to America? _____
_____

3. From what country did the first large wave of Jewish immigration come? _____

4. To what extent did Jewish settlers participate in American life?
_____

5. What promoted a vast second wave of Jewish immigrants, this time mainly from Russia? _____

6. What stemmed the tide of immigration of Jews to the United States? _____

7. In which neighborhood of what city did most of the newcomers choose to live? _____

IN ISREAL

Fill in the blanks from the words listed below.

The first modern Jewish settlers in Palestine were sixteen members of a group known as _____, who arrived in the year

_____. By 1914 the Jewish population there reached

_____. During World War I, on November 2, 1917, at the

urging of _____ _____, Britain issued its approval of a Jewish national home in Palestine. This document, signed by

_____ _____, is known as the _____

_____. English troops, including three Jewish battalions,

defeated the rulers of Palestine, the _____, who had

controlled the area since 1517. The _____ _____

_____ gave the British control of the Holy Land until people in the area were ready to govern themselves. In the year

_____, however, Britain abandoned its earlier position and

proposed a state dominated by _____, with limited Jewish immigration and land ownership. To deal with the resulting

Arab-Jewish hostilities, the _____ _____ voted to divide the area into two states, one Arab, one Jewish. The first prime

minister of Israel, _____ _____, took office in the

year _____. The Arab nations then attacked Israel in a

conflict which the _____ won. Israelis call this their War of

100

_____. Another war took place in the _____

Peninsula in _____. In 1967, Israeli troops captured the

Golan Heights and the _____ _____ of the Jordan

River and reunited _____ in the _____

_____ War. Peace lasted only until the year _____,

when the Arabs regained territory by attacking Israel on

_____ _____.

Independence	Israelis	1936
Turks	Jerusalem	1973
Chaim Weizmann	Yom Kippur	1956
United Nations	Six Day	1882
League of Nations	Sinai	1948
David Ben-Gurion	West Bank	Balfour Declaration
BILU	90,000	Arabs
Lord Balfour	1967	

SOMETHING TO THINK ABOUT

In what ways have women achieved equality with men in the modern Jewish world?

A MAGEN DAVID CROSSWORD

Across

2. French for "the"
3. Reform founder (initials)
4. first woman
5. Abba ("The Master")
8. Jewish candelabrum
11. Hebrew letter
12. Ancient Hebrew priest
15. sheep's sound
16. heavenly bodies
17. decay
18. Albert
19. leading German-Jewish
    scientist (initials)
20. Hitler's party
23. principle
27. kilogram
29. operate a car
30. upon
31. consume
32. eye
33. preposition
34. obese

Down

1. shield of David
   (2 words)
2. wash
4. the letter M
6. Rav
7. meat
9. corrosion
10. father of Zionism
13. Abraham's nephew
14. pronoun
16. body of water
19. against
21. Promised Land
22. Passover celebration
24. Semitic but not Jewish
25. kindled
26. son of
28. _____ and behold
32. _____ (spoken) Torah
33. preposition

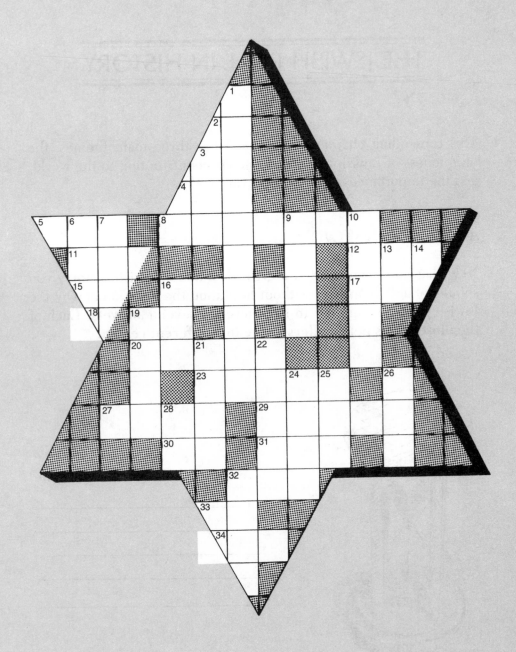

Chapter 26

THE JEWISH ROLE IN HISTORY

This concluding chapter of Volume I has three main themes: the uniqueness of Jewish history, the Jewish contribution to the world, and the importance of Jewish survival.

A UNIQUE HISTORY

Now that you have learned a great deal about Jewish history, you should be able to answer without hesitation the question of why the Jewish people is unique. In fact there are several answers. **Each of the illustrations below offers a clue to a different reason.**

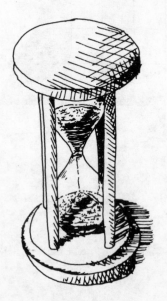

1. Empires have come and gone but _____

_____

_____

_____.

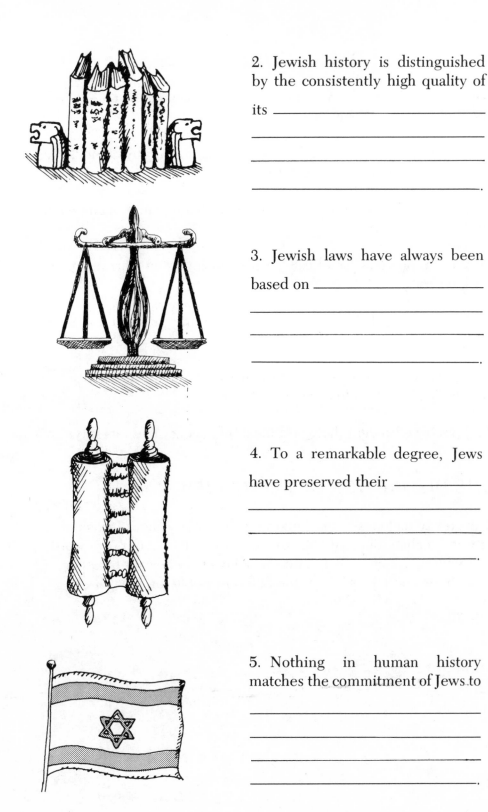

2. Jewish history is distinguished by the consistently high quality of its _____

_____

_____

_____.

3. Jewish laws have always been based on _____

_____

_____

_____.

4. To a remarkable degree, Jews have preserved their _____

_____

_____

_____.

5. Nothing in human history matches the commitment of Jews to

_____

_____

_____

_____.

THE JEWISH CONTRIBUTION

All but *one* of the following statements are known to be true. Circle the number next to the *false* one.

1. The Jewish people sowed the seeds of democracy by demolishing the idea that rulers could be gods.

2. Jewish monotheism led to the belief in the equality of all people in the eyes of God.

3. The Prophets of Israel called on nations to stop warring and to seek peace.

4. Judaism taught that all people are inherently sinful and must be taught to be good.

5. Jews have set an example for the world by dedicating themselves to building a better life here on earth.

6. Jews have brought the world ideals of decency and morality.

THE DISTINCTION OF BEING A JEW

Chapter 26 includes a very important short essay about Jewish identity and feeling different because one is Jewish. In your own words, tell why you believe it is important for every Jew to take part in Jewish life and take pride in the difference of being Jewish.

ANSWER KEY

This key gives answers to questions, exercises, and puzzles based on facts in the textbook. Except in special instances, it does not provide answers to those questions which require the student to paraphrase material from the book or to interpret an idea or express an opinion.

Chapter 1

HOW JUDAISM TOOK ROOT *Fill in* 2000 2000 B.C.E 165 B.C.E Biblical One God Mesopotamia Ur Haran Sarah Lot Canaanites Israelis Egypt nation **MAP STUDY** 1. Mesopotamia Egypt Canaan 2. Ur Haran Shechem Beersheba **EMPIRES AND NATIONS** *True or false* 1. T 2. T 3. F 4. T 5. F 6. T *Place in order* 1. Egyptian 2. Assyrian 3. Babylonian 4. Persian 5. Greek 6. Roman **THE CALENDAR** 1. B.C. = Before Christ A.D. = Anno Domini B.C.E. = Before the Common Era C.E. = Common Era 2. Jews disagree that Jesus was either the Messiah or the Lord (Christ means Messiah, Domini means Lord) 3. a

Chapter 2

A PEOPLE IN BONDAGE *Unscramble* Promised Canaan Egypt Pharaohs taxed monuments Raamses *Combined letters* Exodus **A FREE PEOPLE** *Fill in* Moses Exodus 1225 B.C.E. Red Sea refugees Egypt Canaan thirteenth covenant Ten Commandments Sinai ethical 1000 **A NATION BEGINS TO TAKE FORM** *Multiple choice* 1. c 2. b 3. b. 4. b 5. b 6. a 7. b 8. b **A NATION RULED BY KINGS** 1. Saul 2. David 3. Solomon

Chapter 3

IN THE NORTHERN KINGDOM *Fill in* 1. Northern Kingdom 2. Amos 3. Assyrian 4. farming 5. rituals 6. Bible 7. Mesopotamia 8. ten **IN JUDAH** *True or false* 1. F 2. T 3. T 4. T 5. F 6. T **THE PROPHETS SHAPE JEWISH VALUES** *Underline* 1. responsibility 2. just 3. Nebuchadnezzar 4. exile covenant 5. mistreating the poor 6. Isaiah *Match* 9 3 4 7 2 6 1 5 8

Chapter 4

RETURN OF THE EXILES *Circle* 3 7 **THE JEW IN ANCIENT GREECE** *Match* 5 2 4 1 3 **JEWISH REBELLION** *Fill in* 1. Judah Maccabee 2. Mattathias 3. Antiochus 4. Temple 5. Hanukkah

Chapter 5

ROME EXPANDS *Multiple choice* 1. c 2. b 3. b 4. b
NATURE OF THE EMPIRE *Circle* 2 8
A BIBLICAL CROSSWORD PUZZLE

THE MANY NAMES OF THE PROMISED LAND Canaan Judea
Palestine Eretz Yisrael Zion Israel

Chapter 6

JUDEAN CONQUEST *Fill in* Hasmoneans 100 John
Hyrcanus Idumea Judaism Salome Alexandra 63 B.C.E.
Pompey ten **HEROD'S REIGN OF TERROR** *True or false*
1. F 2. T 3. F 4. T 5. T **BE AN EXPERT** *Underline*
1. Qumran caves 2. 1947 3. Biblical texts and commentaries 4. 2000

years   5. Essenes   **FACTIONS IN JUDEA**   1. Zealots
2. Essenes   3. Sadducees   4. Pharisees   **THE TEACHERS**
Hillel   Shemaia or Avtalion   Shammai   Hillel

Chapter 7

HISTORY MAKERS   *Matching*   6   3   1   2   5   4   7/
JEWS UNDER TYRANNY   *Fill in*   Herod   procurators   Judea
Pontius Pilate   Jesus   Florus   Zealots   Nero   66 C.E.
73 C.E.   Galilee   Josephus   Zealot   Titus   Vespasian   ninth
Av   70 C.E.   **THE MESSIAH IDEA**   *True or false*   1. F   2. T
3. F   4. T   5. T   6. T   **YEARS OF CONFLICT**   *Sentence*
completion 1. b   2. a   3. b   4. a   5. a

Chapter 8

A REMARKABLE STORY   *Unscramble*   Zealots   Jerusalem
Judaism   Vespasian   Torah   Jewish Law   rabbis   *Combined*
letters   Oral Torah   **WHAT YAVNEH BROUGHT**   *Circle*   5
7   **JEWISH HEROES**   *Matching*   Bar Kochba   Johanan ben
Zakkai   Rabbi Joshua ben Ḥananiah   Rabbi Akiva   **KNOW YOUR**
HISTORY   *True or false*   1. F   2. F   3. T   4. F   5. T   6. T

Chapter 9

DEVELOPMENT OF JEWISH LAW   1. Mishnah   2. Gemara
Mishnah   Gemara   **THE SPREAD OF LEARNING**   *True or false*
1. F   2. T   3. F   (not Mishnah but Gemara)   4. T   5. T
WORDS THAT BEAR WEIGHT   *Matching*   6   1   4   5   3
2   **VALUES TAUGHT BY THE RABBIS**   *Multiple choice*   1. b
2. b   3. b   4. a   5. b   6. a

Chapter 10

BIRTH OF A NEW RELIGION   *Fill in*   seventh   Islam
570 C.E.   Mecca   camel driver   Judaism   Christianity   Allah
Medina   Jews   Arabs   holy war   Muslims   **THE TEACHINGS**
OF MUHAMMAD   *True or false*   1. F   2. T   3. F   4. T
5. F   6. T   7. F   8. T

Chapter 11

JUDAISM FLOURISHES *Fill in* 1. Masoretic 2. Jerusalem
3. Africa 4. Geonic **WORDS OF WISDOM** *Unscramble*
Yisrael Geonim Babylonia responsa scribe Masora
Genizah *Combined letters* learning **A RELIGIOUS CONFLICT**
Multiple choice 1. c 2. c 3. b 4. b 5. c **JEWS OF**
SPAIN *Circle* 2 6

Chapter 12

JEWISH SCHOLARSHIP IN SPAIN *Matching* 5 4 1 3
2 **DEVELOPMENTS IN THE GOLDEN AGE** *Underline* 1. less
2. Russia 3. Toledo 4. Jews

Chapter 13

THE DARK AGES *Fill in* Roman Muslim Western Europe
500 1000 Germanic Christian Charlemagne Holy Roman
Empire Eastern Europe Vikings Scandinavia **JEWS IN**
CHRISTIAN EUROPE *Circle* 1. c 2. b 3. b **HOW JEWS**
FARED *True or false* 1. T 2. F 3. F 4. F 5. T **MAP**
STUDY *Circle* Cordova Toledo Troyes Mainz Khazar
Empire **ASHKENAZIC OR SEPHARDIC?** 1. A 2. S 3. A
4. S 5. S 6. A 7. S 8. A 9. A 10. S **A MAN OF**
RENOWN Rashi

Chapter 14

FROM IGNORANCE TO HIGH CULTURE *Fill in* High Middle
Ages 1000 1450 Christianity Europe kings nations
knighthood witch burning castles Renaissance 1450 1520
Roman Catholic **DOUBLE CROSTIC** *Vertical* Dark Ages
Christopher Columbus Spaniards rebirth burn secret Jew
Roman Catholic Sistine Chapel medium aevum in Italy Leonardo
da *Across* The Middle Ages and Renaissance produced a remarkable
culture which continues to play a major part in our lives.

Chapter 15

THE CRUSADES *Multiple choice* 1. a 2. b 3. c 4. a
5. b 6. a **MAN OF VALOR** Naḥmanides

Chapter 16

ITALY *Circle* e **ENGLAND** *Multiple choice* 1. a 2. c
3. b 4. a 5. c 6. a **FRANCE** 1. Jews were free to learn and
earn. 2. persecution 3. for their skills 4. two centuries 5. wear
special clothing and a badge **SPAIN** *Complete* 1. Marrano
2. Inquisition 3. auto-da-fé 4. Torquemada

Chapter 17

REMAINING JEWISH *Matching* 6 4 1 2 5 3 *True
or false* 1. T 2. F 3. T 4. T 5. F 6. T **THE
KABBALAH** *Unscramble* Kabbalists zeal Jews comfort
universe *Combined letters* Zohar *Check* b

Chapter 18

CHRISTIANITY SPLITS *Fill in* Martin Luther Protestant
Reformation German Roman Catholic Church Protestantism
Counter-Reformation Christian intolerance 1618 Thirty Years'
War 1648 Christianity tolerant ghettos **A CHANGING
WORLD** *Complete* 1. Lutherans 2. sun 3. Index of Prohibited
Books 4. divine right **ENLIGHTENMENT** *True or false* 1. T
2. F 3. F 4. T

Chapter 19

THE GHETTO SYSTEM *Circle* 4 6 11 12 **CREATORS
AND CREATIONS** *Matching* 2 1 4 3 6 5
YIDDISH *True or false* 1. T 2. T 3. T 4. T 5. F
JEWS OF PRAGUE AND ROME *Complete* 1. attacks, fires, heavy taxes,
anti-Jewish laws, expulsions 2. Jews could deal only in used goods
3. permission to live in their own homes

Chapter 20

A "LITTLE GOLDEN AGE" *Multiple choice* 1. c 2. a 3. b
4. a 5. b 6. b 7. a **THE NETHERLANDS** *Complete*
1. Catholic Spain 2. Protestantism 3. Amsterdam 4. sea trade
5. Menasseh ben Israel 6. Oliver Cromwell **LANDS OF HOPE**
Match 5 7 9 10 8 2 6 3 4 1 **JEWS IN
THE NEW WORLD** 1. suffered persecution 2. Netherlands 3. Jews
who settled in New Amsterdam

Chapter 21

EASTERN EUROPEAN JEWS *Multiple choice* 1. c 2. b 3. a
4. c 5. a 6. c 7. b **THE FALSE MESSIAH** *Complete*
1. converting 2. the Holy Land (or any other word for the Promised Land)
3. Messiah 4. death conversion (Islam) 5. shock (or such words as
horror or anger)
WORD SEARCH

```
O R L B C D P O E R S N
P I L P U L O K M K D N
P E X O Y R W E J   N C
P C R L K E B H L O   I T
O L A A M E D I N O R A
R U B N V D W I L P Q R
T S C D C G J L F Q R C
U I W S K C A S S O F O
N O F T H A L H E G B M
I   F R S J O P Q S T B E
T O X N O I T A C U D E
Y N X
E B C U R X I V U Z A D
```

Chapter 22

REACHING GOD *Unscramble* poor superstitious Almighty
feelings dancing zeal love education Hasidism *Name*
Baal Shem Tov **THE OPPOSITION** 1. False 2. Poland; was great

scholar   3. b   4. They began to understand and be more tolerant of one another   **MOSES MENDELSSOHN**   *Multiple choice*   1. a, c   2. b   3. a   4. b, c   **COURT JEW**   *Circle*   6   **EIGHTEENTH CENTURY**   *Matching*   6   8   2   10   4   9   1   5   3   7

Chapter 23

THE JEWISH CONTRIBUTION   1. Israel was seeking admission to the international community.   2. wealthy Jewish patriot who contributed to the American Revolution   3. United States   4. oldest synagogue in the New World   5. a. Karl Marx   b. Albert Einstein   c. Sigmund Freud/   **MODERN HISTORY**   *Fill in*   American Revolution   1775   monarchies   aristocracy   Industrial Revolution   democracy   markets   colonies   World War I   Russia   depression   1930's   Poland   World War II   Soviet Union   oil producing   Third World

Chapter 24

HISTORICAL HIGHLIGHTS   *Multiple choice*   1. b   2. c   3. a   4. c   5. a   6. b   **NEW APPROACHES TO JUDAISM**   *Matching*   1. c, a, d, b, e   2. c, d, e, a, b   **DREYFUS AND HERZL**   *Fill in*   1. homeland   2. Alfred Dreyfus   3. nineteenth   4. traitor   5. anti-Semitism   6. *The Jewish State*   7. First Zionist Congress   8. 1948   9. Holocaust   **THE RISE OF HITLER**   1. Yes   2. No   3. No   4. No   5. No   6. Yes

Chapter 25

JEWS UNDER COMMUNISM   *Circle* 4   **THE LAND OF THE CZARS**   *True or false*   1. F   2. T   3. F   4. F   5. T   6. T   7. F   **IN AMERICA**   1. First Amendment   2. governments crushed liberal movements   3. Germany   4. joined in every area of American life   5. pogroms   6. immigration laws passed after World War I   7. Lower East Side of New York   **IN ISRAEL**   *Fill in*   BILU   1882   90,000   Chaim Weizmann   Lord Balfour   Balfour Declaration   Turks   League of Nations   1936   Arabs   United Nations   David Ben-Gurion   1948   Israelis   Independence   Sinai   1956   West Bank   Jerusalem   Six Day   1973   Yom Kippur

A MAGEN DAVID CROSSWORD

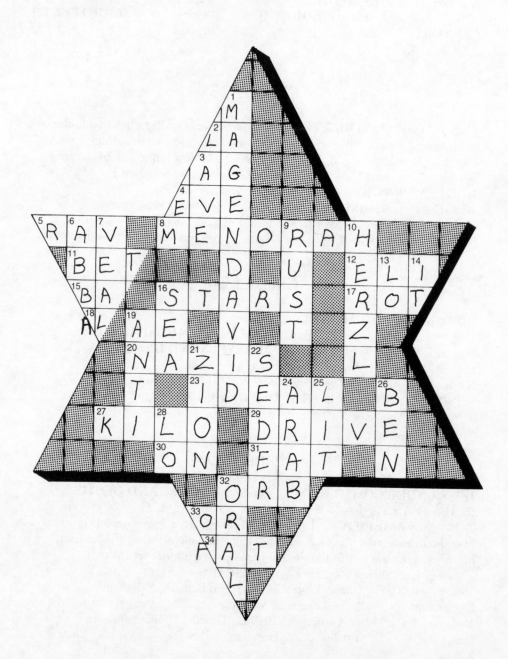

Chapter 26

A UNIQUE STORY   1. the story of the Jewish people continues
(hourglass)   2. intellectual and spiritual life (books)   3. high ethical standards
(scale of justice)   4. basic principles and traditions (Torah)   5. the idea of the
Promised Land (Israeli flag)   **THE JEWISH CONTRIBUTION**
Circle   4